Stretch your KS2 SPaG skills with CGP!

This book is perfect for pupils aged 10-11 who are confident with the Grammar, Punctuation and Spelling skills they need for Year 6.

It's filled with challenging questions to help them gain a deeper understanding of each topic. We've also included mixed practice quizzes and a test at the end so pupils' strengths and weaknesses can be assessed.

And there's more! Everything is perfectly matched to the National Curriculum and you'll find answers to every question at the back. Enjoy!

What CGP is all about

Our sole aim here at CGP is to produce the highest quality books — carefully written, immaculately presented and dangerously close to being funny.

Then we work our socks off to get them out to you — at the cheapest possible prices.

Contents

Grammar

Section 1 – Word Classes

Section 2 – Verb Forms

Section 3 – Phrases and Clauses

Section 4 – Linking Ideas

Section 5 – Writing Style

End of Grammar Quiz

Punctuation

Section 6 – Sentence Punctuation

Section 7 – Commas and Apostrophes

Section 8 – Punctuation for Speech

Section 9 – Paragraphs and Layout

End of Punctuation Quiz

Contents

Published by CGP

Written by Joanna Copley and John Svatins

Editors: Andy Cashmore, Eleanor Claringbold, Christopher Lindle, Sam Norman, Gabrielle Richardson, Hannah Roscoe and Caroline Thomson

With thanks to Jan Greenway for the copyright research.

A note for teachers, parents and caregivers

Just something to bear in mind if you're choosing further reading for Year 6 pupils — all the extracts in this book are suitable for children of this age, but we can't vouch for the full texts they're taken from, or other works by the same authors.

ISBN: 978 1 78294 948 0

Clipart from Corel®

Printed by Elanders Ltd, Newcastle upon Tyne.

Based on the classic CGP style created by Richard Parsons.

Section 1 — Word Classes

Nouns: Subjects and Objects

Nouns and noun phrases can either be the subject or the object in a sentence.

The words in green are all doing the verb. This makes them the subject of the sentence.

Jamil kicked the ball.

The dog bit my foot.

James and Robin watched a film.

The words in red are all having the verb done to them. This makes them the object of the sentence.

The verbs in these sentences are in black.

1 Circle the <u>subject</u> or <u>subjects</u> of each sentence.

The subject of the sentence can be more than one word.

The (elephants) stood at the watering hole.

(Martin) took the jacket and put it in the wardrobe.

On Tuesdays, (Zane) goes to band practice. ✓

(Poppy), (Joe) and (Ella) bought chocolate.

As well as the piano, my (sister) plays the drums.

(Ben) washed the dishes while (Amanda) cleaned the worktops.

2 Tick the sentences which contain <u>objects</u>.

My dad grows tomatoes. ✓ ✓

Flowers grow in the park. ☐

Nitin moves his shoulders. ✓ ✓

Dean moves very slowly when he's tired. ☐

The shop closes at 5 pm. ☐

She closed the door when she left. ✓ ✓

Most pronouns change depending on whether they're the subject or the object of the sentence.

I love dinosaurs. They fascinate me.

The subject pronoun 'I' changes to 'me' when it is the object of the sentence.

3 Fill in the table of <u>subject</u> and <u>object pronouns</u>.

Subject Pronoun	Object Pronoun		Subject Pronoun	Object Pronoun
I	→ *Me* ✓		we	→ *us* ✓
you	→ you ✓		*the*y →	*the* m ✓
he	→ *him* ✓			
She	→ her ✓			
it	→ *it* ✓			

If you're struggling, try putting the pronouns into the sentences about dinosaurs above.

4 Circle the <u>subject pronouns</u> and underline the <u>object pronouns</u> in this sentence.

(We) ✓ should really have gone to see <u>them</u>, but (I) just couldn't face (it) ✓

5 Explain why the sentence below is not grammatically correct.
Use the terms '<u>subject pronoun</u>' and '<u>object pronoun</u>' in your answer.

Cathy and me went to Italy.

Jaxon and I went to itay. ✓

How did you find nouns and pronouns that can be the subject or the object of a sentence? Tick a box.

 ✓ ✓ ✓

Word Class and Word Function

Sometimes it's hard to tell what class a word belongs to (e.g. noun). You can only tell by looking at how the word is used in a sentence — its function.

> I fell hard on the ground. ⟵ hard as an adverb ✓
>
> The exam was really hard. ⟵ hard as an adjective ✗

1 Write down whether the <u>underlined</u> words are used as <u>adverbs</u> or <u>adjectives</u>.

I <u>bought</u> my <u>Grandad</u>'s <u>weekly</u> magazine for <u>him</u>   *adverb's* ✓   ✗

The helicopter <u>flew</u> <u>low</u> over the leafless trees.   *adverb* ✓ ✓

He was so <u>tired</u> that he couldn't walk <u>straight</u>.   *adverb* ✗ ×adverb

I <u>take</u> my neighbour's dog out for a walk <u>daily</u>.   *a* ✗ ×adverb

2 In the sentences below, the made-up word 'wimble' is used as <u>two different</u> <u>word classes</u>. Say what you think the word classes are, and explain <u>why</u>.

> Today two wimbles flew into the house.   Word class: ....

I think this because: ....

....

> Sorry, I was too busy wimbling.   Word class: ....

I think this because: ....

....

3 Now write your own sentence using the word 'wimble' (or a word derived from 'wimble') and give its <u>word class</u>.

I couldn't wimble...

....   Word class: ....

Common words like 'this', 'these', 'those' and 'that' can be particularly tricky.

I have never seen that boy. ⟵ **This** points out a particular **boy**. **It is a determiner.**

I don't think that he will go. ⟵ **This** joins ideas. **It is a conjunction.**

I hate that! ⟵ **This** replaces a noun (or noun phrase). **It is a pronoun.**

4 Give the **word class** of the underlined word in each sentence below.

*Think about the **function** of the underlined word in the sentence.*

I don't want you to <u>take</u> <u>those</u> books away. ....

She said <u>that</u> she didn't want <u>to</u> eat breakfast. ....

<u>I</u> really enjoyed <u>that</u>. ....

Would you mind if <u>I</u> borrowed <u>this</u> book? ....

I really like <u>that</u> bracelet. ....

I haven't seen <u>these</u> before. ....

5 Write sentences which contain the words shown below.
Say which **word class** the underlined word belongs to in each sentence.

.... <u>that</u> people

Word class:
That

<u>These</u> trousers ....

Word class:
these

....

Word class:

.... <u>those</u>.

those

CGP — not to be photocopied

Section 1 — Word Classes

Words can also change their function over time.

The word 'text' was originally a noun. ⟹ A text is a piece of written work.

When mobile phones developed text messages, 'to text' also became a verb. ⟹ We text each other every day.

6 Write a sentence of your own that uses the words below in a <u>different word class</u> from their original use. You may need to add <u>letters</u> or a <u>suffix</u> to the word. The first one has been done for you.

'medal' — originally a <u>noun</u>, now sometimes used as a <u>verb</u>

The Olympic athlete had never medalled before, but now he has won a silver.

'mobile' — originally an <u>adjective</u>, now often used as a ....

'book' — originally a <u>noun</u>, now often used as a ....

7 The expression 'But me no buts!' is used to stop someone raising objections. Explain how this expression plays with the <u>word class</u> of the word '<u>but</u>'.

A bit aglary anagry by the text.

Were you able to identify and use words which belong to more than one word class? Tick a box.

Synonyms and Antonyms

Synonyms are words that are **similar** in meaning.

old ➡ antique, ancient, aged   problem ➡ difficulty, dilemma

Synonyms must belong to the **same word class:**

climb ➡ ascend, mount, steep ✗

verb   'steep' is an adjective, so it can't be a synonym of 'climb'.

1) <u>Underline</u> all the words on each line that are <u>synonyms</u> of the first word.

good: sing, great, assist, kind, excellent, happy, saint

pretty: beautiful, attractive, neat, sparkle, lovely, cute

sharp: point, piercing, acute, razor-edged, unpleasantness

bright: white, gleaming, shine, glaring, intelligent, cheerful

poor: inadequate, weakness, feeble, ineffective, hungry, penniless

Remember that words can have more than one meaning.

2) Find <u>two synonyms</u> for each of these words.

small   ....

finish (verb)   ....

dull   ....

trip (noun)   ....

stone   ....

brave   ....

laugh (verb)   ....

Section 1 — Word Classes

10

3 For each sentence, write some effective <u>synonyms</u> for the <u>underlined word</u>.

Nabila saw the enraged bull <u>moving</u> towards her like an express train.

synonyms: ....

Dan gasped in astonishment as the <u>big</u> pterosaur spread its wings.

synonyms: ....

Malia <u>said</u>, "Don't make a single sound! If it hears us, it will kill us!"

synonyms: ....

Antonyms are words which have the **opposite** meaning to each other.
They can be used to **create a contrast** in a sentence.

While George enjoyed life in his luxurious mansion,
Eve endured a miserable existence in her pitiful shack.

---

4 Change the <u>underlined</u> words to a suitable <u>antonym</u> and write the new sentence underneath.

Gwen <u>smiled</u> as the clowns began their <u>amusing</u> routine.

....

Each <u>evening</u> at <u>sunset</u>, the Inca priest turned to the <u>west</u>.

....

The road through the forest was <u>wide</u> and <u>straight</u>.

....

Niall was <u>reluctant</u> to go and <u>dawdled</u> down the road.

....

10

5 Create your own <u>thesaurus entries</u>, like the one below.

> **beautiful** (adjective)
>
> Synonyms: gorgeous, delightful, handsome
>
> Antonyms: ugly, unattractive, hideous

Writers use a thesaurus to find synonyms and antonyms. The words are set out like this.

> **friend** (.......................)
>
> Synonyms: ...., ..., ...
>
> Antonyms: ...., ..., ...

> **give** (.......................)
>
> Synonyms: ...., ..., ...
>
> Antonyms: ...., ..., ...

> **quickly** (.......................)
>
> Synonyms: ...., ..., ...
>
> Antonyms: ...., ..., ...

6 Write a sentence which includes a word and its <u>antonym</u>, to create a <u>contrast</u>.

....

....

Can you use synonyms and antonyms? Tick a box. ☹ ☑ ☺ ☑ ☺ ☑

Section 2 — Verb Forms

Modal Verbs

Modal verbs express certainty, ability and obligation.
Here are some examples:

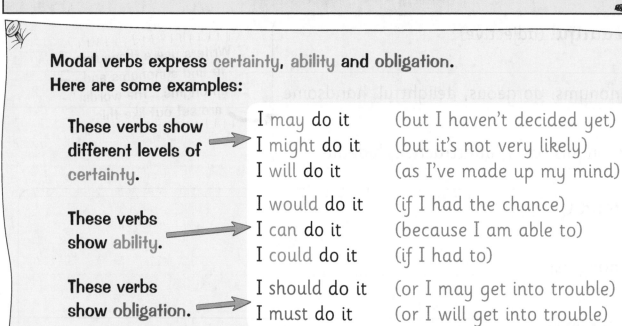

These verbs show
different levels of
certainty.

I may do it   (but I haven't decided yet)
I might do it   (but it's not very likely)
I will do it   (as I've made up my mind)

These verbs
show ability.

I would do it   (if I had the chance)
I can do it   (because I am able to)
I could do it   (if I had to)

These verbs
show obligation.

I should do it   (or I may get into trouble)
I must do it   (or I will get into trouble)

1 Draw lines to match each sentence containing a **modal verb** to the correct label.

She might be going out to lunch.

He was suggesting I should tidy my desk.

I would do it if someone showed me how.

They will be taking a holiday next week.

We can sit here; there's plenty of room.

We may live to regret that.

She could climb it if she wanted to.

We must get to the airport early today.

Certainty

Ability

Obligation

2 Write your own sentences using modal verbs to express **certainty** and **obligation**.

certainty: ....

obligation: ....

     © CGP — not to be photocopie

3 Circle modal verbs expressing <u>certainty</u>. Underline modal verbs of <u>obligation</u>.

I was so sunburned that I knew I couldn't go to the beach. Mum told

me I could have asked for the sun-cream the day before, and she would

have given it to me, and then I might not have caught the sun so badly.

"You should have reminded me," I grumbled. "Anyway, I must use it

next time before we go out."

"You should," said Mum. "You may want to stay indoors today."

4 Fill in the gaps in the passage below with suitable <u>modal verbs</u>. Make sure you use a <u>variety</u> of modal verbs.

There are many possible answers.

You could keep guinea pigs in a hutch, but it .... be

nicer if they .... run about. They .... get

sick in a small cage. You .... put them in a larger run

as they .... do with a lot of exercise to keep them fit.

They .... have water and plenty of hay. Keep two

together, or they .... be lonely and sad.

5 Write a sentence using modal verbs to express <u>ability</u>, <u>certainty</u> and <u>obligation</u>.

....

....

....

How did you find using modal verbs to express certainty, ability and obligation? Tick a box.

The Subjunctive

The subjunctive form is used to create an alternative reality:

> If Phil were taller, he could reach it.

This is the subjunctive form. It makes you imagine that Phil was taller.

The subjunctive is also used for actions which are not certain to happen:

> I insisted that he pay his bill and leave.

These are in the subjunctive form.
You can't be sure from this sentence
whether he actually did pay his bill and leave.

1 Here are some sentences which use the <u>subjunctive</u>.
Match each sentence to the <u>reason</u> the subjunctive has been used.

Oh dear! If only I <u>were</u> a tidier person!

If he <u>were</u> a gentle cat, I'd stroke him.

I insist that they <u>be</u> informed
of this development.

If you <u>were</u> to move school, I'd miss you.

I requested that she not <u>be</u>
prosecuted for the offence.

We'd go out if you <u>were</u> properly dressed.

Your recommendation, madam, that the
rules <u>be</u> relaxed is frankly unthinkable.

They suggested that I <u>go</u> home directly.

"If he <u>were</u> more amenable,"
I said, "I'd help him."

Not certain
to happen

Alternative
reality

Section 2 — Verb Forms

2 In each pair of sentences, tick the one that uses a <u>subjunctive</u>, and underline the <u>subjunctive form</u>.

As she is willing to speak, I shall let her speak. ☐

If she were willing to speak, I would let her speak. ☐

I suggested that he consult a lawyer. ☐

I am sure that he consulted a lawyer. ☐

If she was embarrassed, she didn't show it. ☐

If she were embarrassed, she would show it. ☐

3 Fill in the gaps in the sentences below with a <u>subjunctive</u>. There may be more than one correct answer.

If I .... you, I would not fight with James.

His insistence that the building .... torn down was ignored.

It is out of the question that this newspaper .... that story.

If Jenny .... more resilient, she might have weathered this storm.

I'd rather have stayed at home, if truth .... told.

The judge ordered that the defendant no longer .... detained.

4 Write your own sentence using a <u>subjunctive</u>.

....

....

....

Can you identify and use the subjunctive? Tick a box. ☹ ✓ 😐 ✓ 🙂 ✓

Verb Forms – Recap

There are lots of verb forms you need to know.

These can all be found in the glossary at the back of the book.

One form you may not have met yet is the imperative form:

    Buy the latest phone!   Be the envy of your friends!

The imperative is used to give commands. You can recognise an imperative because the verb does not have a subject.

1 Circle all the <u>imperative</u> forms in the sentences below.

The bookcase is about to fall. Hurry up and move out of the way!

Stop using plastic, or we'll never be able to clean up the seas.

Make sure she knows that I didn't do it to make her cross.

I have to put the mixture in now, so pass me the cake tin.

2 Write three sentences which include an <u>imperative form</u> that your teacher might say to the class during the school day.

....

....

....

3 Write your own sentences that use each type of <u>verb or verb form</u> below.

 Use the glossary at the back of the book to help you.

Simple present: ....

Present progressive: ....

Simple past: ....

Past progressive: ....

Present perfect: ....

Past perfect: ....

Modal verb: ....

'If' the subjunctive: ....

'Demand' the subjunctive: ....

Imperative: ....

4 Write the script for a TV advert for this state-of-the-art mobile phone. Use at least <u>one imperative</u> and at least <u>three other verb forms</u>. Say which verb forms you have used.

....

....

....

....

....

....

....

....

The verb forms I have used are: ....

....

....

Verb Forms in Action

If your verb forms are always the same, your writing will seem a bit dull:

> I went swimming. Then I walked home.
> Then I did some piano practice.

Using a variety of verb forms will often make it more engaging for the reader:

> After I had finished swimming, I walked home.
> Since then, I have done some piano practice.

(1) Read the passage and then answer the questions below.

> I woke up feeling rather sad as my friend had gone on holiday. I wanted to go too but Mum wouldn't let me after I'd fallen off my bike while I was riding with no hands.
>
> "I've been good ever since," I said to her at lunchtime. "I didn't mean to do it, and I'm being very careful not to break anything else. It was only one bone."
>
> "I never know what you will get up to next," sighed Mum. "If I were to let you go, you'd only come home with another one. Be thankful you're not grounded to stop you going out at all!"

Find a past perfect verb: ....

Find a present perfect verb: ....

Find a subjunctive verb form: ....

Find a present progressive form: ....

Find an imperative form: ....

Find a past progressive form: ....

When you write a story, try asking yourself these questions before you start:

- What had happened before your story starts?
- How is your character feeling? (e.g. regrets, hopes, fears)
- What are the decisions that your character has to make?
- What might the consequences of those decisions be?

This will help to make your writing engaging, with a variety of verb forms.

2 Write the opening of a story about someone's first day at secondary school. Think about the questions above to ensure you get a variety of verb forms.

....

....

....

....

....

....

....

3 Write down the names of at least three of the verb forms you've used in your story.

Can you identify different verb forms, and use them in your writing to make it more engaging? Tick a box.

Section 3 — Phrases and Clauses

Modifiers

Words, phrases and clauses in a sentence often modify other words, phrases or clauses. That means they give you more information about them.

dusty shelf ⟵ The adjective 'dusty' modifies the noun 'shelf'.

the pen that I borrowed ⟵ The relative clause 'that I borrowed' modifies the noun phrase 'the pen'.

When I grow up, I want to be a singer. ⟵ The subordinate clause 'when I grow up' modifies the main clause 'I want to be a singer'.

If you understand exactly what is modifying what in your writing, you will be able to write more clearly, and build more sophisticated sentences.

1 <u>Circle</u> the word, phrase or clause in each sentence which is <u>being modified</u> by the underlined words.

I lay for some time on the <u>immaculate</u> lawn.

It was <u>extremely</u> hot in the direct sunlight.

John, <u>who wasn't a very fast runner</u>, was easily chased down by Paul.

<u>Although it was late</u>, she was determined to complete the task.

The underlined words are 'modifiers' of whatever you circle.

2 <u>Modify</u> the underlined word or phrase with the type of word, phrase or clause in the box.

(adverb) the .... <u>strong</u> wind

(preposition phrase) <u>the house</u> ....
....

(relative clause) <u>Zac</u>, ...
...., suddenly appeared.

© CGP — not to be photocopie

Sometimes it can be unclear what a word, phrase or clause is meant to be modifying.

> Bob painted Mo in the garden. ←── **It's not clear who is in the garden — Bob or Mo.**

You'll often need to **reword** your sentence to remove the **ambiguity**.

3 It is not clear which part of the sentence the underlined <u>modifier</u> in the sentence below is modifying. Explain how this makes the meaning <u>unclear</u>, and suggest two ways you could reword the sentence to <u>remove the ambiguity</u>.

Exercising <u>often</u> makes you feel happier.

The meaning is unclear because ....

....

....

Ways to reword the sentence: ....

....

....

....

4 Explain this joke. Include the words '<u>modifier</u>' or '<u>modifies</u>' in your answer.

Person A: "I know a girl with a pet mouse called Steve."
Person B: "Oh yes, and what's the mouse called?"

....

....

....

Were you able to understand how words, phrases and clauses modify each other? Tick a box. ☹ ☑ 😐 ☑ 🙂 ☑

Modifying the Subject

You can often combine two sentences into one sentence by modifying the subject.

See page 4 if you need a reminder of what a 'subject' is.

For example, although this is fine as two sentences... →

> Paz has been a keen cyclist for some years. He has recently invested in a new bike.

... this single sentence flows better:

> Paz, a keen cyclist for some years, has recently invested in a new bike.

This noun phrase modifies the subject of the sentence (Paz). It is separated from the main clause by commas.

1 Rewrite these sentences as **one sentence** with a **noun phrase** modifying the **subject**.

Remember to use commas to separate your noun phrase from the main clause.

Mr Clay had been a smart dresser in his youth. He now wore only jeans.

....

....

Wimbledon is a district of south-west London. It is home to a world-famous tennis tournament.

....

....

Roald Dahl is a much-loved children's author. He was born in Wales to Norwegian parents.

....

....

You can also put the modifiers of the subject at the start of the sentence.

Almost frightening in its grandeur, the house stood isolated on a hill.

This adjective phrase modifies the subject of the sentence (the house).
This is a more prominent position in the sentence, so it really makes
the modifying phrase stand out.

2) For each sentence below, write a <u>modifier</u> for
the subject, using the pictures as a prompt.

....,

Mrs Moody was not a woman to be trifled with.

....,

Grantwich was about to undergo a great change.

....,

the elephants went back to the oasis.

....,

the war was a source of adventure for Arthur.

Can you use phrases to modify the subject of a
sentence to make your writing flow better? Tick a box.

Phrases and Clauses – Characters

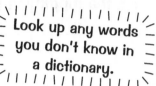

 Good writers use modifying phrases and clauses to introduce characters. This lets the reader learn a lot about them in a short space of time.

1 Read the opening of the novel 'Emma' by Jane Austen below, then complete the questions about it.

Look up any words you don't know in a dictionary.

> Emma Woodhouse, handsome, clever, and rich, with a comfortable home and happy disposition, seemed to unite some of the best blessings of existence; and had lived nearly twenty-one years in the world with very little to distress or vex her.

Which <u>three adjectives</u> modify the subject 'Emma Woodhouse'?

....

Which <u>noun phrase</u> sums up all Emma's good fortune?

....

Which <u>adverbial</u> modifies the verb 'lived'?

....

2 Write your own passage, in the style of the extract above, about <u>yourself</u>. Start with your name, then <u>modify it</u> with some phrases and clauses.

....

....

....

....

....

3 Read the extract below from the novel 'Great Expectations' by Charles Dickens, which describes a <u>scary character</u>. Then answer the questions below.

> A fearful man, all in coarse grey, with a great iron on his leg. A man with no hat, and with broken shoes, and with an old rag tied round his head. A man who had been soaked in water, and smothered in mud, and lamed by stones, and cut by flints, and stung by nettles, and torn by briars; who limped, and shivered, and glared, and growled; and whose teeth chattered in his head as he seized me by the chin.

In the extract above:

- Underline the phrases starting 'with...' which modify 'man'.

- Underline three relative clauses which modify 'man'.

- Explain the <u>effect</u> that this <u>build-up</u>

  Think about the feelings of the boy who has been 'seized' by the chin.

  of modifiers has on the reader.

....

....

....

4 Imagine your own scary character. Describe what the character looks like, using a <u>build-up</u> of different phrases and clauses.

You could repeat 'a man...' like in the Q3 extract.

....

....

....

....

....

How did you find using phrases and clauses to write a vivid description of a character? Tick a box.

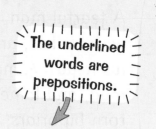

Phrases and Clauses – Settings

Using a variety of modifying phrases and clauses will help you set the scene in your writing.

When describing a scene, good writers often include relative clauses **which start with a** preposition:

...the angry cries of the mob, <u>over</u> which she could just about hear...

...an old bookshop, <u>beside</u> which was a narrow alley...

These help your writing to flow better, and allow you to build a more complex picture as you set the scene.

(1) Read this short passage about Parkgate, a village in the northwest of England. Underline the two <u>relative clauses</u> which begin with a <u>preposition</u>.

Formerly a port on the River Dee estuary, Parkgate is now a popular destination for ice-cream eaters and bird-watchers. It has a long row of historic buildings, in front of which a sandstone wall forms a barrier against high tides. The estuary is now a vast salt marsh, beyond which visitors can see an attractive stretch of the North Wales coastline.

(2) Write a passage about your own town like the one above. Start with a <u>noun phrase</u> which <u>modifies</u> the name of your town, and include <u>at least two relative clauses</u> which begin with a <u>preposition</u>.

....

....

....

....

....

3 Read this extract from 'The Secret Garden' by Frances Hodgson Burnett, describing a journey. Then answer the questions below.

> On and on they drove through the darkness, and though the rain stopped, the wind rushed by and whistled and made strange sounds. Mary felt as if the drive would never come to an end and that the wide, bleak moor was a wide expanse of black ocean through which she was passing on a strip of dry land.

Underline the three verbs or verb phrases which describe the 'wind'.
How do they help to create a <u>mood</u> in this passage?

....

....

Underline the relative clause which starts with a proposition.
What does this sentence tell us about Mary's <u>feelings</u>?

....

....

4 Rewrite the description of Mary's journey so that the mood is <u>more cheerful</u>. Start with a sentence about the weather, and then construct a sentence similar to the one above ('Mary felt as if... through which...').

....

....

Mary felt as if ....

....through which

....

....

Can you use phrases and clauses effectively to set the scene in your writing? Tick a box.

Section 4 — Linking Ideas

Ways to Link Ideas

Linking your ideas clearly shows the logic of what you're saying. Here are the main ways you may want to link ideas in your writing and some examples.

Time	Place	Cause
whenever next then meanwhile	nearby under opposite	since because due to

Addition	Contrast	Condition
also additionally as well as indeed	however whereas although despite	if as long as unless whether

1 Underline the <u>linking word</u> or words. Say what type of link it is. The first one has been done for you.

<u>After</u> the rain fell, the path became muddy. ➡ ....time..................

Beside the stream was a small cottage. ➡ ....

Tidy it — whether you want to or not! ➡ ....

We'll go out whenever you're ready. ➡ ....

She likes coffee; I, however, like tea. ➡ ....

They went for a walk despite the rain. ➡ ....

We ate pizza as well as salad for lunch. ➡ ....

Provided that I can afford it, we'll go. ➡ ....

Put it down gently because it's fragile. ➡ ....

I disliked the visit, whereas she didn't. ➡ ....

I've had enough; moreover, I feel sick. ➡ ....

Section 4 — Linking Ideas

2 Rewrite each pair of sentences so that they're <u>linked</u> in the way given in <u>brackets</u>. The first has been done for you.

We might drive to the beach. Will the car start? (condition)

We could drive to the beach as long as the car will start.

Some people agree with me. Other people don't. (contrast)

....

I want to go swimming. The weather might not be fine. (condition)

....

Some people approve of homework. They think it's useful. (cause)

....

3 Write a sentence of your own using the <u>type of link</u> given in brackets.

(cause) ....

(addition) ....

(time) ....

(place) ....

(contrast) ....

(condition) ....

(any two of the above) ....

....

....

How did you find linking ideas by time, place, cause, addition, contrast and condition? Tick a box.

Linking Ideas in Different Genres

You tend to find different types of links in different genres of writing. For example, instruction texts will often have lots of links of time to tell the reader the order they need to do things in.

> First, open the case. Once you have checked the pieces are all present, lay them on the floor in small piles.

A genre is a particular type of writing.

1 Read the <u>texts</u> and answer the <u>question below</u>.

Alien Abduction   Genre: Story

The following morning, Mai went to milk the cows as usual. From a little way off, she could see the gate to the barn was open, and when she went in, the cows were nowhere to be found. First she looked for them in the field. She could see hoof prints all around her, but by the time she reached the middle of the field, there were none. In the distance she could see her mum running towards her, waving her arms. Suddenly she heard a strange buzzing noise overhead.

Shiny Shirts Ltd   Genre: Report

2018 has been a good year for Shiny Shirts Limited. Despite the rising cost of raw materials, the company's finances are in good shape, thanks to a doubling in sales over this period. Indeed, sales through the website have nearly tripled. Unlike our competitors, we have managed to keep costs down, and as a consequence our profit levels have remained healthy. Furthermore, we have invested in new machinery, which should help next year's performance.

Write down any <u>linking words</u> and <u>phrases</u> that you can find in 'Alien Abduction'. Group them according to the type of link (e.g. 'Place', 'Contrast').

2 Write down all the <u>linking words</u> and <u>phrases</u> that you can find in 'Shiny Shirts Ltd'. Group them according to the type of link (e.g. 'Place', 'Contrast').

3 Use your answers to Questions 1 and 2 to complete the sentences below about the <u>types of links</u> you get in <u>story writing</u> and <u>report writing</u>.

In story writing, you tend to find more links of ....

...., whereas in report writing you tend to find more

links of ....

I think this might be because in stories it is important to show

.... ,

whereas in reports it is important to show ....

....

4 Give <u>two types of links</u> you'd expect to find in a <u>persuasive text</u>.
Write some examples of <u>linking phrases</u> and <u>clauses</u> you may expect to find.

1.	2. ....
Examples:	Examples: ....
....	....
....	....

Can you understand how and why different types of links are used in different genres of writing? Tick a box.

Linking Ideas Across Paragraphs

Linking words can be used to link or contrast ideas across paragraphs.
In non-fiction, these will often be links of addition, contrast or cause — these
help your reader to understand the structure of what is being explained to them.

1 Read the paragraphs below about male and female lions.
Add appropriate linking words or phrases to the gaps in the text.
Then in each box say what <u>type of link</u> it is (addition, contrast
or cause), and explain <u>what exactly is being linked</u>.

Male lions weigh up to 250 kg when fully grown.
They have a mane, while females, which weigh in at about
190 kg, do not. Males drive other males away from their group
of lionesses, and can be aggressive towards juvenile male lions.

Females, ..., are the more efficient
predators. Hunts are usually carried out by groups of lionesses
working together to bring down the prey.

Type of link: ....

What is being linked: ....

....

...., lionesses cooperate in
caring for cubs, even those that are not their own. Lionesses will
defend their young cubs from any half-grown males that threaten
to kill them.

Type of link: ....

What is being linked: ....

....

2 Write three paragraphs about whether you think it's better to <u>walk to school</u> or <u>go by car</u>. Jot down <u>brief notes</u> for each paragraph in the boxes below, and the type of link you are going to use between each paragraph.

Paragraph 1:

⬇ Link type: ....

Paragraph 2:

⬇ Link type: ....

Paragraph 3:

....

....

....

....

....

....

....

....

....

....

....

Can you identify and use links between paragraphs to show addition, contrast and cause? Tick a box.

Repetition and Ellipsis

Repetition is used to hammer home the point you're trying to make:

> Well, some of the wallpaper stuck to the wall. It also stuck to the ceiling, it stuck to the chair, it stuck to the table, it stuck to my socks and it stuck to Dad's hair. Marvellous.

The repetition emphasises how sticky the wallpaper was, and what a mess was made.

Ellipsis is the opposite of repetition. It's when you leave words out:

> I can play chess and Dwayne can too.

You don't need to repeat 'play chess' here. You know the reader will understand the sentence without it.

---

1 Put 'E' or 'R' in the box to identify <u>ellipsis</u> or <u>repetition</u> in each sentence below. Write <u>two new sentences</u> at the bottom — one to show ellipsis and one to show repetition.

I've seen the film but Rita hasn't. ☐

He tried this, he tried that and he tried the other. Nothing worked. ☐

They sold the house because they wanted to. ☐

Anne has eaten too much, and Mia too little. ☐

I want to go, I want to go now and I want to go for a long time. ☐

.... | E

....

.... | R

....

2 **Rewrite the dialogue below using <u>ellipsis</u> to make it less repetitive.**

"Come on. Let's go to Dave's."
"I don't want to go to Dave's. It was really boring last time."
"I know it was really boring last time, but it might not be really boring this time. And if we don't go to Dave's, we'll just be bored here."

....

....

....

....

....

....

3 **Below is a half-time team talk by a captain on the sports field. Does it contain <u>ellipsis</u> or <u>repetition</u>? Explain the <u>effect</u> that this technique is designed to have on the team.**

"I know you're tired — I'm tired too. But we just need one last push: one last push to get us over the line. So when your legs are burning and your lungs are bursting, just remember everything we've trained for, everything we've all worked so hard for. One last push is all we need, and then we can return home champions."

....

....

....

....

Can you use ellipsis and repetition? Tick a box.

Summary of Cohesive Devices

Linking words and phrases, repetition and ellipsis are all cohesive devices — they help your writing to flow better, and form a coherent whole.

Using a variety of cohesive devices (rather than lots of 'ands' and 'buts') will make your writing more sophisticated.

1 Rewrite these short sentences using <u>cohesive devices</u> to make the text <u>flow</u>. Then pick out <u>one cohesive device</u> you used, and <u>say why</u> you used it.

The weather was bad. A cold, stormy wind blew. The wind howled in the chimney. Rain lashed the window. Inside the room, it was freezing. Mari shivered. Draughts came through the rotten window frame. Her bed felt damp. It smelt musty too. Her thin pyjamas didn't keep her warm. There was a bump. There was another bump. There was a shrill, wailing cry. A light flickered through the room. Mari froze with fear.

....

....

....

....

....

....

....

....

....

I used: .... to ....

....

2 In this text there are many uses of 'and' and 'but', which makes it quite boring. Rewrite the text using different <u>cohesive devices</u> to make it <u>more sophisticated</u>.

The ghost wailed and Mari shivered and she could hear it getting nearer so she decided to run but then it was even nearer and cold fingers pulled at the sheet and stroked her hair and then she screamed loudly and then Mum came in and turned the light on and there was nothing there.

....

....

....

....

....

....

3 In your own words, summarise what you have learned about <u>cohesive devices</u> in this section. Say <u>when</u> you think they should be used, and <u>why</u>.

....

....

....

....

....

....

Can you use a range of cohesive devices to make your writing more coherent and sophisticated? Tick a box.

Section 5 — Writing Style

Active and Passive Voice

In active sentences, the subject of the sentence does something to the object.

> Slugs ate the lettuces.
> subject   object

In passive sentences, something is done to the subject.

> The lettuces were eaten by slugs.
> subject

The word 'by' can introduce who or what does the action.

---

(1) In the boxes write **'A'** for the active sentences and **'P'** for the passive ones.

The cat chased the mouse. ☐   Jan was told off by her mum. ☐

The bird was caught by a net. ☐   He was eaten by a crocodile. ☐

Sam was allowed to do the task. ☐   She slipped in the mud. ☐

Josh worked hard at school. ☐   We were beaten by enemies. ☐

Megan enjoyed playing rugby. ☐   They were cheated out of it. ☐

(2) Rewrite each sentence, changing it from active to passive.

Nathan played the trumpet.

....

One goat and two sheep ate all the grass.

....

Lots of people read the article in the paper.

....

The **passive** is useful when you don't want to say **who** did something.

"I'm afraid some ink has been spilt on the carpet," he said sheepishly.

The person speaking doesn't want to say **who** spilt the ink.

3 Imagine you've been playing football in your neighbour's garden and left behind a <u>trail of destruction</u>. Write your neighbour a <u>note to explain</u> all the things that have been <u>ruined</u>. Use the <u>passive</u> to avoid getting yourself in trouble.

Dear Mr Milleridge,

As we all know, in real life, you'd ask permission before destroying your neighbour's garden...

Unfortunately, ...

....

....

....

4 Why do you think we are not told who carried out the action in the sentences in red boxes below? Match up each sentence to the <u>most likely</u> reason (in a blue box).

The carvings were made in prehistoric times.

It's not important who did the action

Fruit should be eaten daily.

Avoiding responsibility

It applies to everyone

A sign will be put up in the morning.

We don't know who did the action

I'm afraid the window has been smashed.

How did you find identifying and using the passive voice, and understanding why it is used? Tick a box.

Choosing between Active and Passive

Some genres of writing use the passive more than others.
For example, in a write-up of a scientific experiment, the reader
wants to know what was done, rather than who did what.

A funnel with filter paper inside was placed in the neck of a bottle.
A mixture of soil and water was poured into the funnel and was allowed
to filter through slowly. The funnel was covered to reduce evaporation.

Using the passive voice means the reader only gets the relevant information.

1 In the box below is a description of part of a scientific experiment.
Rewrite it in the <u>passive voice</u>, so the reader only gets the <u>relevant</u> information.

Joe cut a piece of beetroot into a 1 cm cube. Grace poured some
water into a beaker until it was 5 cm deep. Joe put the cube of
beetroot into the beaker and started a stopwatch. After two minutes
had passed, Mrs Singh took a sample of water from the beaker.

....

....

....

....

....

....

....

2 Imagine you're a police inspector. <u>Summarise</u> these two witness statements, using the <u>passive voice</u> to protect the identity of your witnesses.

Witness 1: "I saw him run into the bank just before 12:30. I heard two gunshots at 12:40 exactly. At 12:43 I saw him run out of the bank and down the street towards the cathedral."

Witness 2: "I heard a man shouting 'Out of my way!' I chased after him through the foyer and pushed him to the ground, but he managed to get away. That's when I rang the police. I think it was around 12:45."

Just before 12:30, the suspect was seen ....

....

....

....

....

....

3 Both of the passages below are written in the passive voice. Which do you think would be better in the <u>active</u> voice? Explain your answer.

1. "A small but noticeable rise in carbon dioxide levels has been observed, but it is not yet known what has caused this change."

2. "The ball has been passed by Nuttall to Sykes, and has been headed in by Lopez! The match has been won by Sideham City in extra time..."

I think passage .... should be written in the active voice because

....

....

How did you find choosing when to use the active voice and the passive voice? Tick a box.

Formal and Informal Register

Register means the type of language which is appropriate for a situation. The language used in informal situations has different features from language used in formal situations.

Informal language

> Sayeed, lend us a pencil, can you, mate? I've broke mine.

Here are some features you're more likely to find in informal language:

- contractions ('I've')
- question tags (see next page)
- slang ('mate')
- non-Standard English ('I've broke')
- idiomatic language (see next page)
- active voice

Formal language

> Please, Mrs Roberts, may I borrow a pencil? I have broken mine.

Here are some features you're more likely to find in formal language:

- people's titles ('Mrs Roberts')
- Standard English
- passive voice
- the subjunctive (see p.14-15)
- more formal vocabulary

1 Read the sentences below and <u>decide which register</u> should be used for each situation. In the boxes write '<u>F</u>' for <u>formal</u> and '<u>I</u>' for <u>informal</u>. At the end write two more situations — one for formal register and one for informal.

A letter of complaint about a game you bought that arrived broken. ☐

Trying to persuade your head teacher to reduce class homework. ☐

Writing in your own diary about a school trip that you really disliked. ☐

Writing an article for a school newsletter about a school trip. ☐

Sending an email to a friend about arranging a birthday party. ☐

Writing a newspaper report about school traffic in your area. ☐

Writing to parents asking them to park more carefully near school. ☐

.... F

.... I

One feature of informal speech is question tags.
These are used to check that your listener agrees with what you're saying.

"I wasn't going to just leave him there, was I?"

Another feature of informal speech is the use of idioms.
These are expressions which aren't meant to be taken literally.

"That song's really doing my head in."   "He must be off his trolley."

---

2 Change each sentence below from <u>formal</u> to <u>informal language</u>. Add question tags, idioms or other features of informal language from page 42.

It appears as if she is extremely angry.

Looks like she's completely flipped her lid.

It might help to imagine saying these things to a friend, brother or sister.

Do you agree that the weather is much hotter today than yesterday?

....

Do you think he is running the risk of being late?

....

Please don't be angry — I'll attend to you shortly.

....

3 Write what someone might say to a friend about their bike breaking on the way back from school. Use as many features of <u>informal language</u> as you can.

....

....

....

Section 5 — Writing Style

4 Below is an extract of someone talking about plastic packaging. Rewrite it as a <u>formal letter</u> to your MP, asking them to discuss the subject in Parliament.

"The thing is, we all say we're worried about all that plastic cloggin' up the oceans, don't we? But when it comes to actually doing something about it, people just bury their heads in the sand. First off businesses are gonna have to stop using needless packaging. And they're gonna have to stop pretending it's OK to cover stuff in non-recyclable plastic. What's wrong with wrapping things in a bit of paper, anyway? Oh, and then councils are gonna have to be clear about what can be recycled and what can't. Don't know about you, but I'm forever buying things thinking I can recycle the packaging, only to find I can't."

Dear ....,

I am writing to speak to you about the important subject of plastic

packaging. ....

....

....

....

....

....

....

....

....
Remember to finish your letter correctly in a formal register.

....

Can you understand and use the different features
of formal and informal language? Tick a box.

Grammatical Features of Different Genres

You can identify different genres of writing, not only by their content, but also by the grammatical features they use.

1 Label each passage (A-D) with the appropriate <u>genre</u> from the box below. Then draw a line to match each passage to the box on the right which best describes its <u>grammatical features</u>.

instructions   poetry   recount   report

A Genre: ....
Through the dark a sound was heard
Whispers soft and inky black

- Sentences start with an imperative.
- Written in the second person.

B Genre: ....
Tigers are the biggest species of the cat family and can reach a length of 3.3 m.

- Words and phrases written in a non-standard order.
- Each line starts with a capital letter.

C Genre: ....
Place part A on your frame and attach with the screws provided. Tighten until firm.

- Adverbials show the sequence of events.
- Written in the first person and past tense.

D Genre: ....
After lunch, we followed the path to the beach and split into three groups.

- Written in the third person with technical vocabulary.
- Present tense.

Were you able to identify the grammatical features of different genres of writing? Tick a box.

Section 5 — Writing Style

End of Grammar Quiz

(1) **Underline the <u>subject</u> and circle the <u>object</u> of each sentence.**

A small man came in and picked up the book.

Mia and Patrick tidied the extremely messy room before lunch.

1 mark

(2) **Circle the <u>adverb</u> and underline the <u>adjective</u> in each sentence. The words to choose from are in bold.**

Skating is **hard**, and the first time I went, I fell **hard** on the ice.

Clara drove extremely **fast** because it was a very **fast** car.

1 mark

(3) **Rewrite the sentence using a <u>synonym</u> for the <u>underlined word</u> and an <u>antonym</u> for the word in <u>bold</u>.**

As I am <u>kind</u>, I won't tell Mum you broke her **newest** vase.

....

....

1 mark

(4) **Add four different <u>modal verbs</u> into the passage so it makes sense.**

I .... not pick that plant; it .... be poisonous. You

.... get very sick, and you .... end up in hospital.

1 mark

(5) **Change each sentence below so it <u>uses the subjunctive</u>.**

If I was a better runner, I might try a marathon.

....

They insisted the ice cream was served immediately.

....

1 mark

6 Write a short passage which uses the <u>past progressive</u>, <u>simple past</u> and <u>present perfect</u> forms.

....

....

....

1 mark

7 Write a sentence that uses the ideas from the sentences below and includes a <u>relative clause</u>.

Theo likes cooking with eggs. He keeps chickens to lay the eggs.

....

....

1 mark

8 Change the <u>active sentence</u> into a <u>passive sentence</u>.

The landslide knocked down many trees.

....

1 mark

9 Change the <u>informal language</u> in these sentences into <u>formal language</u>.

Hey, can I get a new exercise book here? Mine's well full up.

....

1 mark

10 Write a <u>noun phrase</u> which contains a <u>relative clause</u> to describe the <u>landscape</u> in the photo effectively.

....

....

1 mark

I scored [ ] out of 10.

End of Grammar Quiz

Section 6 — Sentence Punctuation

Colons for Lists

Colons can be used to introduce items in a list.

We visited the following cities: Cardiff, Bristol, Exeter and Truro. ✓

The bit before the colon needs to be able to stand on its own as a full sentence.

Then we will visit: Leeds, York, Hull and Whitby. ✗

This is incorrect, because 'Then we will visit' isn't a full sentence.
It should be: 'Then we will visit Leeds, York, Hull and Whitby'.

---

1 Add any <u>missing colons</u> and <u>commas</u> to the sentences below.

We had everything we needed for the cake eggs flour butter and sugar.

The results of our birdwatch were five starlings two sparrows three robins and one crow.

His acting roles came in this order 'Deadly Hamsters' 'Night of the Killer Crabs' 'Deadly Hamsters 2' and 'Revenge of Fluffy'.

---

2 Rewrite these sentences using the word '<u>following</u>' and a <u>colon</u> before the list.

The people coming to my party are Tom, Yasmin, Ellen, Tomas and Deena.

....

....

They speak Spanish in Chile, Argentina, Mexico, Peru and Bolivia.

....

....

Can you use a colon to introduce a list? Tick a box.

Using a Semi-Colon in Lists

If a list contains long phrases or clauses, a semi-colon can be used instead of commas to prevent confusion.

> The wizard had three choices: ask the king, who never showed mercy, to show mercy; make himself invisible and hope that they went away; or run for his life.

Unlike lists with commas, you need a semi-colon before the last item.

1 Add **three more** detailed items to each list. **Separate** them using **semi-colons**.

The guest list was unusual: an Albanian juggler called Pavel; ....

....

....

....

The police inspector had four suspects: a singer, who was spotted near the

robbery; ....

....

....

My dream house would contain the following things: a robot that brought

cheeseburgers to my bedroom; ....

....

....

How did you find using a semi-colon to separate long phrases or clauses in a list? Tick a box.

© CGP — not to be photocopied

Section 6 — Sentence Punctuation

Semi-Colons to Join Clauses

You can use semi-colons to show a close link between two main clauses.
These main clauses should both be able to stand as sentences on their own.

| Squash is a fast game. | | Bowls is much slower. |

Squash is a fast game; bowls is much slower.

Semi-colons can take the place of a co-ordinating conjunction.

I eat lots of fruit but I'm not keen on vegetables.

I eat lots of fruit; I'm not keen on vegetables.

1 **Rewrite these sentences by replacing a <u>conjunction</u> with a <u>semi-colon</u>.**

That ride was too scary so I'll be sticking to the dodgems in future.

....

....

I like my friends to be funny and clever, but I'll make an exception for you.

....

....

2 **Write <u>two sentences</u> that contain two <u>main clauses</u> linked by a <u>semi-colon</u>.**

1. ....

....

2. ....

....

Section 6 — Sentence Punctuation

© CGP — not to be photocopied

3 Work out if the semi-colon has been used <u>properly</u> in each sentence. Put a <u>tick</u> in the box if it is correct and a <u>cross</u> if it is wrong.

Evie, Ben and Arthur; you're all in my team. ☐

Wait for the last day of the sales; they end on Friday. ☐

I told Jabir the match was cancelled; he turned up anyway. ☐

You'll get plenty to eat; at the barbecue. ☐

The traffic was terrible; we arrived with a minute to spare. ☐

A semi-colon can also be used when the second clause starts with an adverb.

> Heavy snow was followed by icy winds; consequently the first race of the season was cancelled.

4 Add a <u>main clause</u>, and a <u>semi-colon</u> if necessary, to each sentence below.

1. The town had withstood the siege for eight weeks; meanwhile ....

....

2. We saw a trail of crumbs; obviously ....

....

3. ....

.... therefore I might run out of money soon.

4. ....

.... however, her sportsmanship has been sadly lacking.

Can you join two main clauses with a semi-colon? ☹ ✓ ☺ ✓ ☺ ✓

Section 6 — Sentence Punctuation

Colons to Introduce a Clarification

Colons can be used after a statement to introduce a clarification.

statements

We are facing a terrible problem: we have run out of teabags.

Arthur was a thief: a handbag snatcher.

The clarification could be an explanation or a specific example.

1) **Explain what information the word, phrase or clause <u>after the colon</u> gives us.**

He got what he deserved: nothing!

(............... *explains what he deserved* ....)

Unlike semi-colons, colons do not need to be followed by a complete main clause.

Three children were picked for the running team: Anwen, Rob and Jamie.

(....)

The dog was in disgrace: there were ripped clothes everywhere.

(....)

Caitlin was first in the race: she led from the start.

(....)

2) **Continue each of these sentences after the colon.**
Write at least one <u>explanation</u> and at least one <u>specific example</u>.

I had laid out my clothes for the next day: ....

My brother is afraid of so many things: ....

I knew why the sweet jar was empty: ....

I shall be giving you a special gift: ....

3 Put a <u>tick</u> or a <u>cross</u> in each box to show if the <u>colon</u> has been <u>used correctly</u>.

The answer is simple: we eat our way out! ☐

Mr Williams is our neighbour: his daughter is called Jessica. ☐

There are three people in my class who come
to school by bus: Josie, Bhalraj and Imran. ☐

She knew one thing: she would never go back. ☐

Deep in the forest: under the old oak tree, the treasure was buried. ☐

4 <u>Match</u> each sentence to the reason why it is <u>punctuated incorrectly</u>.

I live close to a lake:
I've never swum in it.

I need you to help me with
changing the tyre: on my bike.

Snakes are reptiles cold-blooded:
and egg-laying.

colon in
wrong place

different
punctuation needed

no colon
needed

5 Write your own <u>sentences that use colons</u>. One should use the colon to
introduce an <u>explanation</u> and the other should use it for a <u>specific example</u>.

explanation ....

....

specific example ....

....

Were you able to use colons to introduce an
explanation or a specific example? Tick a box. 😐 ✓ 🙂 ✓ 😃 ✓

Section 6 — Sentence Punctuation

Section 7 — Commas and Apostrophes

Apostrophes for Contraction and Possession

Apostrophes are used for possession **and** contraction.

Apostrophe of possession ('the football of Tariq')

Apostrophe of contraction ('let us')

Apostrophe of possession (Even though 'football' is not repeated, it needs an apostrophe to show that it belongs to Leigh.)

Tariq's football is flat. Let's take Leigh's.

---

1 Add the missing <u>apostrophes</u> to the sentences. In the <u>boxes</u>, write how many apostrophes show <u>contraction</u> and how many show <u>possession</u> in each sentence.

	contraction	possession
When its Emilys turn to do the washing up, shes nowhere to be found.	☐	☐
Jordans dog lost its ball and wont stop howling.	☐	☐
We werent allowed sweets at Hollys, but Kims mum doesnt mind.	☐	☐
I dont know whos sitting in Ellies seat, but theyll be in trouble when she gets back.	☐	☐

---

2 For each sentence, write the <u>underlined contractions in full</u>.

<u>I'd</u> be terrified. <u>Aren't</u> you? ....I would........... ....

<u>Who'll</u> clear up the mess if <u>I'm</u> not here? ....

<u>They're</u> hoping <u>he's</u> left some food this time. ....

Single nouns **ending in an 's' still need an apostrophe and an 's' to show possession.**

the bus's tyres | James's sister

Plural nouns **ending in an 's' do not need an extra 's' to show possession.**

the fairies' castle

Plural nouns **that don't end in 's' need an apostrophe and an 's' to show possession.**

the women's race

---

3 **Write phrases** that use an **apostrophe** to describe each of the things below.

Example: the toys belonging to the dogs .... *the dogs' toys* ....

the tentacles of an octopus ....

the playground of more than one child ....

the den of more than one fox ....

the room of my sisters ....

4 **Circle** the **mistakes** in each sentence then **write** them out **correctly**.

Thomas' sister does'nt know whose coming.

....

My cat keep's leaving it's fur on Mums cushions.

....

The teacher's car park at my school is'nt very large.

....

There going to leave Agnes' song out of the show.

....

Can you explain the function of apostrophes and use them accurately? Tick a box.

☹ ☑ 🙂 ☑ 😊 ☑

Section 7 — Commas and Apostrophes

Commas to Punctuate Adverbials

You often need to add commas to separate adverbials from the main clause of a sentence. Otherwise, it can be hard to know where the adverbial begins or ends.

> After washing the dishes, Carys went outside to ride her bike.

> Ken stomped upstairs, grumbling and muttering, to tidy his room.

Generally you don't need a comma when the adverbial is very short or when the adverbial is at the end of a sentence.

> Sophie walked on tiptoes across the hall.

> Evander attended the ceremony in his best clothes.

Always re-read your work. This will usually tell you whether a comma is needed to make the meaning clear.

1 **Add commas** to the sentences to separate the **adverbials** from the main clause. You might not need to add commas to all of the sentences.

After carefully preparing a canvas the artist began to paint.

Flowers shoot up all over the place at this time of year.

The train pulled out leaving the passenger behind.

The robin was hopping completely unafraid nearer and nearer to the man.

On the other side of the valley the vegetation was much greener.

Bob finally got there and to his astonishment he was the first one to arrive.

After watching the film the girls discussed it over a cup of tea and a biscuit.

2 Add an <u>adverbial</u> from the boxes to each of the <u>main clauses</u>.
<u>Rewrite</u> the whole sentence, making sure you <u>punctuate</u> it correctly.

(having waited for what seemed like ages) (slowly and cautiously)

(riding swiftly into the night) (without a backward glance at the house)

(beyond the blue horizon) (dodging the other team's players)

Hamid charged down the pitch as fast as he could. ...Hamid, dodging the...

....other team's players, charged down the pitch as fast as he could.....

The boy edged out from behind the skip. ....

....

The fawn entered the glade. ....

....

A small, shivering figure walked down the path. ....

....

The knight set off on the adventure of a lifetime. ....

....

3 Write <u>two sentences</u> of your own that include <u>adverbials</u>.
Decide whether or not <u>commas</u> are needed to keep the meaning clear.

1. ....

....

2. ....

....

How did you find punctuating adverbials with
commas to keep the meaning clear? Tick a box.

Commas to Avoid Ambiguity

If a sentence can have more than one meaning, we say that there is ambiguity. A comma can make it clear which meaning the writer intended.

This sentence suggests the pig is on the bike.

> The farmer chased the pig on a bike.

This sentence suggests the farmer is on the bike.

> The farmer chased the pig, on a bike.

(1) Add a <u>comma or commas</u> to each sentence, so that it has the <u>same meaning</u> as the sentence in the box.

The treasure chest contained gold coins diamonds and pearls. → There are four different items in the chest.

The class were visited by Mrs King a retired doctor and a juggler. → The class were visited by a retired doctor and a juggler.

I'm ready to paint Mark. → I am telling Mark that I am ready to paint.

At the village green people are holding a barbecue. → There is a barbecue at the village green.

Molly the school caretaker is locking the gates. → A caretaker called Molly is locking the gates.

2 **Explain** the effect of <u>adding commas</u> to the <u>second sentence</u> in each pair.

Ameena and I saw a fox with a telescope.
Ameena and I saw a fox, with a telescope.

....

....

He took his homework and a cake which he ate on the way home.
He took his homework, and a cake which he ate on the way home.

....

....

I was squashed in the back seat of the car with the dogs, Rocky and Lola.
I was squashed in the back seat of the car with the dogs, Rocky, and Lola.

....

....

3 **Draw a picture** in the <u>box</u> below each sentence to shows what it means.

On the plate were green vegetables and sausages.

On the plate were green vegetables, and sausages.

How did you find placing commas correctly to avoid ambiguity in a sentence? Tick a box.

Parenthesis

A parenthesis is a bit of information added to a sentence that the sentence would make perfect sense without.

Commas are the most usual way to show a parenthesis. → Her car, a beautiful red convertible, was parked outside.

Brackets are used for a digression — extra information which is off on a bit of a tangent. → His car (which I suspect his dad had bought for him) was parked outside.

Dashes show a digression in a text which is not very formal. → Well, his car — a real rusty old heap, I can tell you — was parked outside.

1 Add <u>correct punctuation</u> to each sentence to show the <u>parenthesis</u>.

Clara's aunt who few people liked scowled at the children.

Clara's aunt such a kind woman gave sweets to the children.

Clara's aunt her mother's sister smiled at the children.

2 Write <u>three sentences</u> of your own which show the <u>three ways</u> of punctuating a parenthesis.

1. ....

....

2. ....

....

3. ....

....

Can you choose appropriate punctuation to show a parenthesis? Tick a box.

Punctuating Dialogue

When you write dialogue, it can get a bit repetitive to have a reporting clause every time there is a change of speaker.

"Wow," said Sylvie. "What a day."
"You're telling me," said Molly.
"Shall we head back?" asked Sylvie.
"I thought you'd never ask," said Molly.

To avoid the dialogue being repetitive, you can make characters use each other's names, which tells the reader who must be speaking.

"Hi Rob," said Jack.
"Y'all right, Jack?"
"I've been better."
"Listen Jack, it's no use still worrying about it now. What's done is done."
"I suppose you're right," said Jack, with a sigh.

Remember, if speech is on a new line, the reader will know it's a change of speaker.

---

1 Write your own **dialogue** between **two characters** in which one character **has a problem**, and the other character is **giving them advice**. **Punctuate** the dialogue correctly, and make sure it's always clear to the reader **who is talking**.

....

....

....

....

....

....

....

Were you able to punctuate dialogue correctly and avoid using unnecessary reporting clauses? Tick a box.

Reported Speech and Direct Speech

Mixing reported and direct speech helps to make your writing more varied.

"The treasure is in the middle of the island," said Redbeard, tapping the map with a finger, ← direct speech
"so we'll start digging there and work outwards."
Greenbeard sighed loudly and took the crumpled map from Redbeard. Patiently, he explained to ← reported speech
his friend that this would not work at all.

Remember that you only use inverted commas **for the actual words spoken in** direct speech. **In** reported speech **you** don't need **inverted commas.**

1 In the sentences below, <u>change</u> direct speech into reported speech, and reported speech into direct speech. Remember to <u>punctuate</u> your answers correctly.

"Why aren't you going to football tonight, Edmund?" asked James. "Aren't you feeling well, or are you doing something else?"

James asked Edmund why he wasn't going to football tonight,

and whether he wasn't feeling well or was doing something else.

"Have we got any rope?" Lily asked Ali. "I think we might need some." Ali told Lily that he'd looked for rope, but that he couldn't find any. He said that they might have to improvise and to take the sheet off the bed.

....

....

....

....

....

2 This passage is completely in <u>reported speech</u>. Rewrite the passage, putting some of it into <u>direct speech</u>, using <u>varied synonyms</u> for the word '<u>said</u>'.

Salma and Bo sat with the wizard while he told them how to get to the island. He explained that they had to be careful in the boat because if they dipped their hands or feet into the water while they were crossing the sea, the Mer-folk would know they were there and would seek to destroy them. Salma asked whether there was any defence against the Mer-folk, and Bo wanted to know if weapons would be useful. The wizard told them that weapons would be a bad idea, as they would make the Mer-folk think that the children were hostile. Salma then asked if they should take food, or some sort of present to the Mer-folk and Bo agreed it would be a good thing to do.

....

....

....

....

....

....

....

....

....

....

Can you change direct to reported speech and vice versa, and punctuate it correctly? Tick a box.

Inverted Commas

As well as to show direct speech, you can also use inverted commas to show irony — when the speaker doesn't believe that the words being used to describe something are accurate.

> The two week 'holiday' I spent clearing out the stables was over.

You can use single or double inverted commas, but be consistent — don't switch between the two.

They are also used for the titles of films, books and songs...

> The film 'Up' is animated.

...and to introduce technical terms.

> A bat is able to find its food in the dark using a technique called 'echolocation'.

(1) Add <u>inverted commas</u> to the sentences and <u>explain</u> why you have used them.

Their last single Gobstopper Girls wasn't very successful.

....

Joanne's great deal left me with no money and a pack of stale biscuits.

....

Everyone knew about Elsa's secret hiding place.

....

I played Ratty in our school play, Wind in the Willows.

....

Animals which are active during the daytime are called diurnal.

....

How did you find using inverted commas for a variety of purposes? Tick a box.

Inverted Commas inside Inverted Commas

When you need to use inverted commas inside direct speech, use double inverted commas on the outside, and single inverted commas on the inside.

This quote is inside **direct speech.**

"The book I read was called 'Revenge of the Purple Aliens'," Hugh said to me. "It was such a scary story, I couldn't sleep." He went on, "It described the aliens as 'slimy-skinned decapods with huge glowing eyes'. I don't fancy meeting one."

This is the title of a book, inside direct speech.

The direct speech is inside double inverted commas.

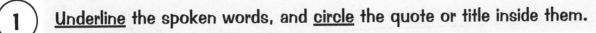

1 <u>Underline</u> the spoken words, and <u>circle</u> the quote or title inside them.

"My ship's called 'Sea Rover' — she's so fast," said the pirate, proudly.

"It says here 'don't feed after midnight', but I did," moaned Jessica.

"I think 'The Greatest Granny' is a brilliant book, don't you?" said Ava.

2 <u>Rewrite</u> these sentences, <u>punctuating</u> them correctly and using the correct <u>inverted commas</u> for any quotes.

I don't know why there was an explosion panted Jim from where he was

lying it says here heat the pot gently and I'm sure that I did

....

....

....

....

Can you punctuate quotes within direct speech?

Improving Paragraphs

Paragraphs organise your ideas so they are clear to your reader.
How you start a paragraph is important, especially in non-fiction texts.

> Comets are not like planets, which are roughly spherical. They are giant, uneven, rocky snowballs, composed of ice and dust. They are a few kilometres wide when they are not near the Sun. As they approach the Sun, the heat from the Sun causes them to develop huge tails of gas and dust. It's these tails which make comets easy to recognise in the night sky.

This first sentence is a topic sentence. It introduces the subject of the paragraph.

The information in blue develops and adds to the information about comets.

The final sentence will often bring the paragraph to some conclusion.

1 **Rewrite** the paragraph so that it's **more organised**. You may need to **change the order** of the information or even **remove** some of the information.

> Sungrazer comets travel so close to the Sun that they can be destroyed. An ellipse is another word for an oval. The orbit of a comet is elliptical. The famous Halley's Comet doesn't get closer than 55,000,000 miles. Comets travel huge distances within the Solar System. Most comets visiting the Solar System travel from beyond the orbit of Neptune.

....

....

....

....

....

....

2 In the box below are some <u>facts</u> about comets, which are written in <u>note form</u>. Use the notes to write an <u>organised paragraph about comets</u>.

> 'Comet' means 'hairy star' — refers to the long tail of gas and dust they develop. Tails develop near Sun. Tails always point away from Sun. Nucleus (centre) of comet is frozen ice/rock — several km across. Tail can be 90 million miles or more long. Comet nucleus also develops a 'coma' near the Sun as it heats up. 'Coma' is made of hot, glowing gases as the nucleus evaporates.

....

....

....

....

....

....

....

3 Imagine you have to <u>teach a friend</u> to write organised paragraphs. <u>Summarise</u> what you have learned on this page in your own <u>organised paragraph</u>.

....

....

....

....

....

....

Section 9 — Paragraphs and Layout

Improving paragraphs is also about the order of paragraphs in a text.
The paragraphs should lead your reader towards your conclusion.

Introduce ➡ Give information in sensible order ➡ Conclude

4 In the box are <u>subheadings</u> for a text about space. <u>Write</u> them out in the <u>order</u> that you would use for the text. (There isn't one correct order. You just need to decide on an order that you think is sensible.)

> The Sun
> Galaxies
> The Universe
> Space
> Comets
> The Earth
> The Moon
> The Solar System

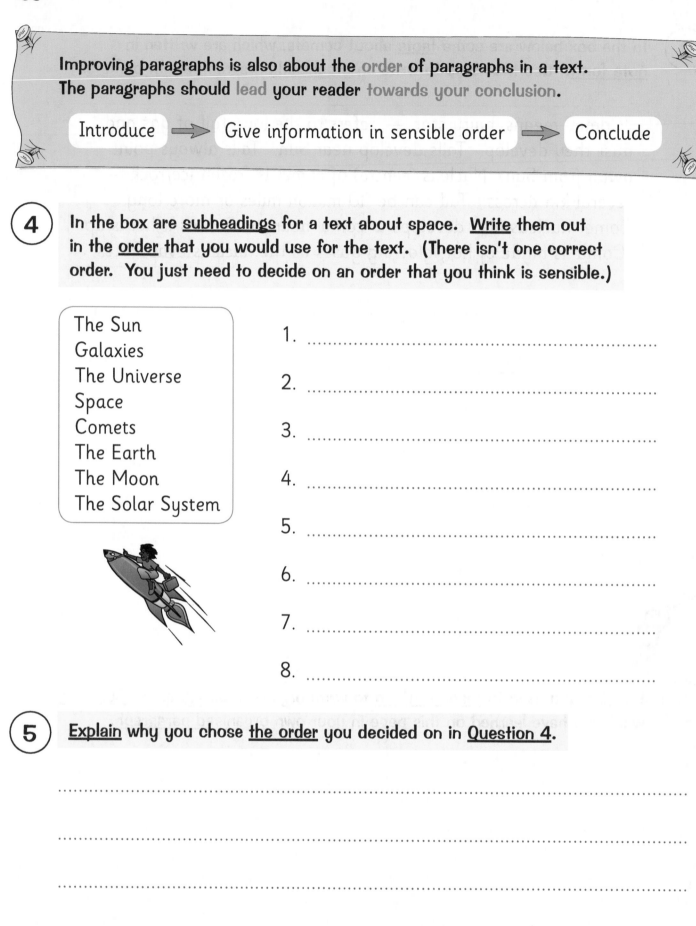

1. ....

2. ....

3. ....

4. ....

5. ....

6. ....

7. ....

8. ....

5 <u>Explain</u> why you chose <u>the order</u> you decided on in <u>Question 4</u>.

....

....

....

....

Can you use paragraphs to organise the information in both the paragraph and the text? Tick a box.

 ☑ ☑ ☑

Bullet Points

Bullet points should be written so that you can read the introduction followed by any of the points, and it should make sense.

Every member of our club should:
· always wear his or her membership badge.
· never speak about the club to non-members.
· the special handshake should always be used.

These two work ok.

This one doesn't work, because you can't say 'Every member of our club should the special handshake...'

When writing bullet points, you also need to make sure the introduction ends with a colon, and that all the bullet points are punctuated consistently.

1 Use the passage below to write a set of bullet points that give advice to tennis players. Write an introduction to the bullet points, and make sure the bullet points are all worded and punctuated correctly.

Tennis Etiquette
    If you disagree on whether a ball was in or out, it's often best to replay the point. Your opponent will appreciate it if you congratulate them when they play a good shot.
    After the match, shake hands graciously with your opponent and thank them. And always remember — it's only a game!

Can you word and punctuate bullet points correctly?

Layout Devices

Layout devices help to make the presentation of a text clear and easy to navigate. They also draw the reader's attention to the most important things.

1 Read the text below. Choose <u>three layout devices</u> used in the text and <u>describe</u> how they help the reader <u>navigate</u> the text.

NEW HEDGE-HOGSPITAL! (Call us <u>free</u> on 0808 157 0136)

Caring for sick hedgehogs

'Hedge-hogspital' is a homing and rescue organisation for sick and injured hedgehogs, and they would like you to know how to deal with one if you find it.

"It's very important not to scare the hedgehog, or make it sicker," said Jen Brown, one of the organisation's vet nurses. "Lots of people feed them milk, as they think hedgehogs like it, but it can kill them, so please don't!"

Help! I've found a hedgehog!

If you find an injured hedgehog in distress, do the following:

1. Find a deep cardboard box and place a hot water bottle wrapped in a tea towel inside it.
2. Wearing gloves, lift the hedgehog carefully and place it into the box.
3. Keep the box in a quiet, dark place.
4. Offer the hedgehog some water, and put some meaty cat or dog food nearby. Don't try to feed the hedgehog directly though!
5. Give the hedge-hospital a call.

....

....

....

....

....

....

2 Create a poster about a subject that interests you, such as a hobby, a club that you belong to or a cause that you think is important. Include the layout devices below and tick them off as you use them.

heading ☐ subheadings ☐ bullet points ☐ illustrations ☐

information in a table ☐ important information in a box ☐

Did you understand why different layout devices are used, and how to use them in your writing? Tick a box.

End of Punctuation Quiz

1 **Add <u>correct punctuation</u> to the sentence below.**

He gave me the following gifts a small white dog with black spots intended to be my travel companion a large loaf of bread which I'd probably never finish and a flask of raspberry lemonade.

1 mark

2 **Add apostrophes of <u>possession</u> and <u>contraction</u> in the correct places.**

Elviss brothers friend said, "Lets take old Sams dog for a walk."

1 mark

3 **Add commas to the sentences to <u>punctuate the adverbials</u>.**

After a very long journey Evie eventually got off the train at Brigg.

The thrush singing like an angel was perched on the tallest tree.

1 mark

4 **Read the sentences. Explain how the <u>position of the comma</u> makes the <u>meaning</u> of the sentence <u>different</u>.**

Please don't pay, Will.

Please, don't pay Will.

....

....

....

1 mark

5 **Which <u>punctuation marks</u> can be used to show a <u>parenthesis</u>?**

....

1 mark

6 Change this <u>reported speech</u> to <u>direct speech</u>.

Salma told her mum proudly that she'd won the maths competition.

....

.... 1 mark

7 Change this <u>direct speech</u> to <u>reported speech</u>.

"Mum, can I miss school?" groaned Dan, unconvincingly. "My

tummy hurts." ....

.... 1 mark

8 Rewrite this <u>direct speech</u> and <u>punctuate</u> it correctly.

That's my dog's ball said Lucy running up to the tall boy and your
dog just chewed it up.

....

.... 1 mark

9 Add a <u>punctuation mark</u> from the box to each sentence below.
<u>Explain your choice</u> of punctuation mark on the dotted line below.

(, ? ! ; . : ")

There was only one possible explanation she'd been kidnapped.

....

Today was a good day tomorrow will be even better.

.... 2 marks

I scored [ ] out of 10.

End of Punctuation Quiz

Section 10 — Prefixes

Roots and Prefixes from Greek and Latin

Many English words come from the languages of the ancient Greeks and Romans. Knowing the meaning of Greek and Latin roots and prefixes can help you work out the meaning of the words you come across.

The 'circum' prefix is the Latin word for 'around'. → circumspect ← The 'spect' root is the Latin word for 'look'.

So circumspect literally means 'looking around'. It is another word for 'vigilant' or 'cautious'.

1 Circle the correct meaning of the underlined part of the word and write down another English word which shares this root or prefix.

Use a dictionary if you're not sure.

psychologist   health / the mind / food   ....

pedestrian   vehicle / roads / foot   ....

photograph   light / people / the land   ....

dormitory   sleep / death / house   ....

millimetre   100 / 1000 / 1,000,000   ....

2 Work out the meaning of the underlined root or prefix.

maternity, maternal   'mater' means ....

benefit, benevolent   'bene' means ....

aquarium, aquatic   'aqua' means ....

mortuary, mortal   'mort' means ....

semi-detached, semicircle   'semi' means ....

telephone, phonetic   'phone' means ....

3 Complete the table by <u>choosing the correct meaning</u> of the root or prefix from the box, and add <u>at least two examples</u> of words which use the root or prefix.

| time | against | air | across | life | believe |
| writing | star | Earth | far away | all | |

Do the ones you know first. Use a dictionary to help you.

Root or Prefix	Meaning	Examples
aer(o)		
anti		
astro		
bio		
chron(o)		
cred		
geo		
graph		
omni		
tele		
trans		

Prefixes: 'em' and 'en'

The prefix 'en' can be used to mean 'to put on' or 'to put into'.

enchain ⟵ This means 'to put into chains'.

It can also be used to make verbs from adjectives and nouns.

adjective → verb

large ⟹ enlarge

The prefix 'em' has the same meaning, but is used as a prefix for words that begin with 'b' or 'p'.

1 Complete the words with '**en**' or '**em**' as a prefix which match the definitions.

to anger: …. …. r …. g ….   to make more bold: …. …. b …. …. …. en

to delight in: …. …. j …. ….   to strengthen: …. …. f …. …. c ….

2 Add an '**en**' or '**em**' prefix to these words and write the word you have created in a **sentence** to show you <u>understand the meaning</u> of the word.

…..power ....

…..close ....

…..danger ....

…..body ....

…..tangle ....

3 Choose a word with the prefix '**en**' or '**em**' to complete each sentence.

I will .... this secret to you, but you mustn't tell anyone!

We had to .... the message so no one else could read it.

I cannot .... this strongly enough. Do not let the cat out!

I wanted to .... in the chess club, but all the places were taken.

Prefixes: 'pre' and 'post'

The prefix 'pre' means 'before' and the prefix 'post' means 'after'.

The postgraduate student worked part-time at a preschool.

This describes someone studying after their first degree.

This describes a place for children before they go to school.

1 Add '<u>pre</u>' or '<u>post</u>' in the gaps and then use the words you have created to <u>complete the sentences.</u>

> ....arranged   ....historic   ....humous
>
> ....pone   ....destined   ....-mortem

In .... times, wolves and bears lived in Britain.

The soldier who died in battle was awarded a .... medal for his bravery.

The meal had been .... to coincide with the cousins' visit.

Due to an outbreak of flu, we had to .... the meeting.

Harold thought he was .... to be king because of a crown-shaped birthmark on his shoulder.

The .... revealed traces of arsenic in the body.

2 The abbreviations 'a.m.' and 'p.m.' stand for the Latin expressions '<u>ante meridiem</u>' and '<u>post meridiem</u>'. Given that you know what '<u>post</u>' means, <u>work out the meanings</u> of the words below.

I think 'ante' means ....

I think 'meridiem' means ....

Prefixes That Require a Hyphen

When the words 'all' and 'self' are used as prefixes, they're usually followed by a hyphen:

> We played on an all-weather pitch.   He's quite self-centred.

The prefix 'ex' can also be followed by a hyphen if it is being used to mean 'former':

> The ex-president still insisted on riding in the biggest car.

(1) Rewrite the sentences <u>changing the underlined parts</u> to words that use the prefixes '<u>self</u>', '<u>all</u>' and '<u>ex</u>'.

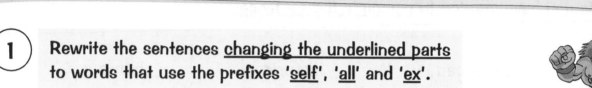

The <u>man who was previously a wrestler</u> <u>worked for himself</u>.

....

The petrol station was <u>one where you served yourself the petrol</u>.

....

<u>The man who used to be her husband</u> went on a holiday <u>where everything</u>

<u>you wanted was included in the price</u>. ....

....

(2) Write the words below <u>in a sentence</u> to show you <u>understand their meaning</u>.

(self-conscious) ....

....

(all-consuming) ....

....

Hyphens may also be used
if adding a prefix would
create an existing word: → re-form ← This means 'form again'.
Without the hyphen,
'reform' means 'improve'.

Hyphens may be used if the prefix ends in
the same vowel as the word it is joining. → re-examine

Prefixes going before a proper noun are also followed by a hyphen:

Having tea without a biscuit felt like an un-British thing to do.

---

3 Complete the sentences by <u>creating words</u> from the prefixes and
root words in the boxes. Use <u>hyphens after the prefix</u> if necessary.

re	dis	re
pre	re	mid
re	dis	re

✚

enter	turn	emerged
appeared	Roman	grace
emphasise	covered	July

In .... Britain, the Celts lived in tribal groups.

Knowing there were mice in there, I refused to .... the shed.

I forgot to .... my library books and received a fine.

"I want to .... the importance of keeping the

classroom tidy," said the teacher. "At the moment it's a ...."

Mum .... her cookbook when the outside became tatty.

The wedding is planned for ....

The fox .... from the bush it had .... into earlier.

4 Explain why a <u>hyphen is needed</u> in the sentence below.

The boss couldn't read all of the names, so he made everyone resign.

....

....

Section 10 — Prefixes

Suffixes: 'able' or 'ible'

It's often hard to know whether to write the suffix 'able' or 'ible', as they sound the same. Here are three rules of thumb to help you decide:

1 Use 'able' if there is a related word ending in 'ation'.

demonstr**ation** ➔ demonstr**able**

2 Use 'able' if the root is or sounds like a complete word.

consider**able**   reli**able**

'consider' is a complete word   'reli' sounds like a complete word

3 Use 'ible' if the root does <u>not</u> sound like a complete word.

ed**ible** ⬅ 'ed' does not sound like a complete word

---

1 Add the suffix '<u>able</u>' or '<u>ible</u>' to the roots below. Write out the <u>full word</u>.

prefer ....   understand ....

justify ....   aud ....

cred ....   fix ....

2 These words with the suffix '<u>able</u>' or '<u>ible</u>' are <u>spelt incorrectly</u>. Use the rules in the green box above to explain why.

suitible ....

horrable ....

irritible ....

intelligable ....

agreeible ....

If the adjective is 'able', the adverb is 'ably' and the noun is 'ability'.

probable   probably   probability

If the adjective is 'ible', the adverb is 'ibly' and the noun is 'ibility'.

possible   possibly   possibility

3 Use the <u>root</u> to form the <u>adjective</u>, the <u>adverb</u> and the <u>noun</u>.

root	adjective	adverb	noun
feas	....	....	....
vary	....	....	....
irritate	....	....	....
vis	....	....	....
excite	....	....	....

4 The words in the box below <u>don't obey the rules</u> from the previous page. Choose <u>three</u> of the words and write them in a sentence.

> sensibly   accessible   reversible
> contemptible   inexhaustible   inevitability

1. ....

   ....

2. ....

   ....

3. ....

   ....

Section 11 — Word Endings and Suffixes

You often have to drop the final 'e' when you add 'able'. ➔ lovable   pleasurable

Words ending with 'ce' or 'ge' keep the 'e' when you add 'able'. ➔ noti<u>ce</u>able   knowledg<u>e</u>able

Words ending with 'g' or 'c' don't need an 'e' when you add 'ible'. ➔ le<u>g</u>ible   for<u>c</u>ible

5 Write the <u>root words</u> below as words ending in '<u>able</u>' or '<u>ible</u>'.

service ....   desire ....

excuse ....   change ....

6 Complete the sentences with words ending in '<u>ible</u>' that <u>make sense</u>. The start of each word is given to you. Use a dictionary if you need to.

Can you write this out again? It's completely **ill**............................ .

He's playing so well, he's practically **inv**............................ at the moment.

I'm afraid he's not **el**............................ to join our club.

Abstract nouns refer to things which are **inta**............................ .

7 Find the <u>correct adjective</u> to complete each sentence and use the word to create a <u>new sentence</u> on the line below.

You'll need to think about which negative prefixes to use.

Something that can't be managed is ....unmanageable............................ .

..My workload this week is totally unmanageable.............................

Something that can't be believed is ....

....

Something that can't be conceived is ....

....

Suffixes: Doubling the Consonant

For words ending in 'fer', you sometimes have to double the 'r' before you add a suffix. It depends on where the stress falls in the word.

Here 'fer' is stressed, so you have to double the 'r'.

preferred

preference

Here 'fer' is not stressed, so you don't double the 'r'.

For words ending in 'el', you always have to double the 'l' when you add a suffix.

travelled

excellent

1) Find the word with the suffix **'fer'** which <u>fits into the gap in each sentence</u> below. To give you a hint the <u>root word</u> is in brackets before each gap.

I've already (transfer) **t**........................... the money.

You decide — I'm (defer) **d**.................. to your better judgement.

My dad said it was (prefer) **p**...................... to use a pedestrian crossing.

I (infer) **i**...................... that he wasn't going to help us.

We need to discuss it. Let's have a (confer) **c**...........................

It was a clear hand ball, but the (refer) **r**...................... didn't see it.

2) Add a <u>suffix</u> from the box below to each word, and use that word <u>in a sentence</u>.

'or'   'ed'   'ous'   'ation'   'ing'

cancel............ ....

counsel............ ....

marvel............ ....

quarrel ....

Section 12 — Confusing Words

Homophones and Easily Confused Words

Homophones are words that are pronounced the same, but which have a different meaning and spelling. You need to learn the correct spelling for each meaning.

guessed ➕ guest

↗ the past tense of guess ↖ a person you have invited

1 Complete each sentence using <u>one</u> of the words from the <u>homophone pair</u>.

bridal / bridle — The .... was fitted over the horse's head.

cereal / serial — There were six episodes in the ....

pray / prey — The tawny owl swooped upon its ....

patience / patients — My .... was tested by the traffic jam.

2 Write a <u>short sentence</u> to show that you understand the meaning of each homophone.

allowed: ....
➕
aloud: ....

lessen: ....
➕
lesson: ....

3 Complete the <u>homophones</u> represented by the pictures below.

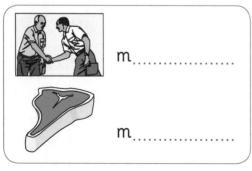

m............................

m............................

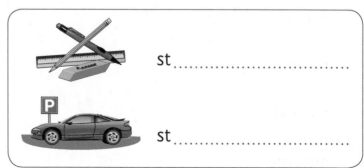

st............................

st............................

© CGP — not to be photocopie

4 Fill in the <u>missing words or definitions</u> for each homophone pair.

.......................: the first version

draught: ....

....

.................: the first part of the day

.........................: ....

....

alter: ....

.................: table used in a church

.........................: run out of energy

.................: a rubber wheel outer

.........................: the part of the body between the ribs and the hips

.........................: unwanted material

.........................: take unlawfully

.........................: ....

....

Although they are not homophones, some words are close enough in spelling or pronunciation to sometimes cause confusion.

| accept / except | breath / breathe | lose / loose |

| desert / dessert | affect / effect | wary / weary |

5 Choose the correct <u>words from the box above</u> to complete the sentences.

It was hard to .... in the smoky room.

The explorers felt .... after trekking through the dry ....

Harry cannot .... that he is wrong this time.

The screw was .... and needed tightening.

The weather may .... the outcome of the match.

'ice' or 'ise'?

Some pairs of homophones (like 'practice' and 'practise') depend on whether the word is a noun or a verb.

The 'ice' form is generally a noun. ⟹ I need some advice.

The 'ise' form is usually a verb. ⟹ Could you advise me?

---

(1) **Choose the <u>correct word from the box</u> to complete the sentences.**

advice / advise   device / devise   licence / license   practice / practise

The council would not .... him to open a market stall.

I .... you not to tease the swans; they will get cross.

The .... for the play went well, but the performance was a disaster!

Burglar Bill tried to .... the perfect plan for his latest robbery.

(2) **Write four sentences of your own. Each one should contain one of the words from the <u>box in Question 1</u> that you didn't use.**

....

....

....

....

Words From the Year 5/6 Spelling List

Below are all the words on the Year 5 and 6 spelling list. By the end of Year 6, you should be able to spell these words correctly.

The following pages will help you learn the most challenging of these words.

1 Put a <u>tick</u>, <u>cross</u> or <u>question mark</u> next to each word to show how <u>confident</u> you are with the <u>spelling</u> of the word.

accommodate	correspond	identity	queue
accompany	criticise (critic + ise)	immediate(ly)	recognise
according	curiosity	individual	recommend
achieve	definite	interfere	relevant
aggressive	desperate	interrupt	restaurant
amateur	determined	language	rhyme
ancient	develop	leisure	rhythm
apparent	dictionary	lightning	sacrifice
appreciate	disastrous	marvellous	secretary
attached	embarrass	mischievous	shoulder
available	environment	muscle	signature
average	equip (-ped, -ment)	necessary	sincere(ly)
awkward	especially	neighbour	soldier
bargain	exaggerate	nuisance	stomach
bruise	excellent	occupy	sufficient
category	existence	occur	suggest
cemetery	explanation	opportunity	symbol
committee	familiar	parliament	system
communicate	foreign	persuade	temperature
community	forty	physical	thorough
competition	frequently	prejudice	twelfth
conscience	government	privilege	variety
conscious	guarantee	profession	vegetable
controversy	harass	programme	vehicle
convenience	hindrance	pronunciation	yacht

2 Add 'ary', 'ery' or 'ory' to complete these words.
Write a sentence using each of the words you have made.

categ.....................

....

cemet...................

....

secret...................

....

necess....................

....

3 Write out the word for each of the definitions below.
The first and last letters are provided for you.

to overstate   ➡   e .... e

cumbersome, mal-coordinated ➡ a .... d

one after the eleventh   ➡   t .... h

an irritant or pest   ➡   n .... e

4 Each box below contains a jumbled word. Each word contains either
'ua' or 'au'. Rearrange the letters and write the correct spelling.

ualivdnid

i..........................

uaseedr

p..........................

uanerstat

r..........................

uangega

l..........................

uateaner

g..........................

5 Add 'ie' or 'ei' to complete these words correctly.

suffic..........nt

consc..........nce

for..........gn

n..........ghbour

misch..........vous

conven..........nce

6 Circle the **correct spelling** in each box.

amature	curiosity	nuisence	criticice
amateur	curiousity	nuisense	critisise
ammateur	cureosity	nuisance	criticise

tempreture	privilege	ryhthm	disastrous
temperature	priviledge	rhthym	disasterous
tempereture	privelege	rhythm	dissastrous

7 The words with blanks have had their **vowels removed** and placed in **clouds**. Put the vowels back into the words and write them out on the dotted lines. You can **cross out vowels** as you use them.

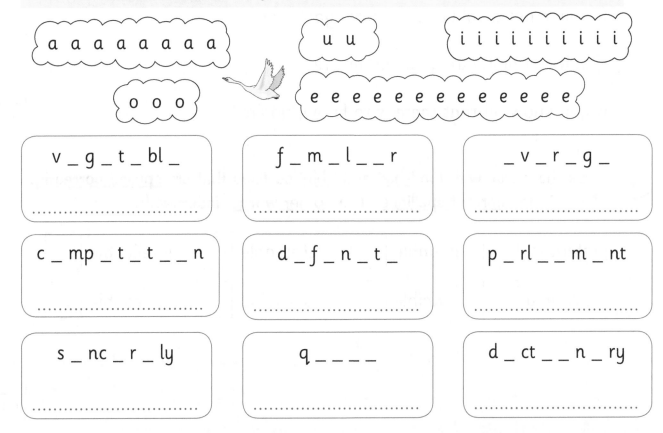

a a a a a a a a a

u u

i i i i i i i i i i

o o o

e e e e e e e e e e e e e e

v _ g _ t _ bl _

....

f _ m _ l _ _ r

....

_ v _ r _ g _

....

c _ mp _ t _ t _ _ n

....

d _ f _ n _ t _

....

p _ rl _ _ m _ nt

....

s _ nc _ r _ ly

....

q _ _ _ _ _

....

d _ ct _ _ n _ ry

....

End of Spelling Quiz

(1) **Write down the meaning of the prefixes below.**

auto = ...   omni = ...

trans = ...   tele = ...

(2) **Match the time periods on the left to the descriptions on the right. Write your own definition for the one that is missing.**

pre-1969   after the fighting was over

post-1066   after the Normans invaded England

pre-lunch   before humans had set foot on the Moon

post-war   ....

(3) **Use a word with a hyphenated prefix to complete these sentences.**

If you're not a soldier any more, you're an ....

If you can motivate yourself, you're ....

If you know all that there is to know, you're ....

(4) **Tick the words with the '-ble' and '-bly' suffixes that are spelled correctly. Rewrite the correct spellings of the other words underneath.**

preferably ☐   audable ☐   accessable ☐   intelligible ☐

irritably ☐   capible ☐   sensably ☐   edable ☐

....

....

5 Turn 'pleasure' and 'knowledge' into their '-ble' forms and write a sentence using the words.

pleasure ➡ ....

....

knowledge ➡ ....

....

2 marks

6 Circle the correct spelling of the underlined words.

We deferred / defered our departure as it was

excellent / excelent weather.

1 mark

7 Use each of the words below in a sentence to show you understand what they mean. You may add any prefixes or suffixes to the words.

affect ....

effect ....

accept ....

except ....

2 marks

8 Fill in the gaps with a 'c' or an 's' so the sentence makes sense.

My advi....e is that you practi....e using this devi....e every day.

1 mark

I scored [ ] out of 10.

CGP — not to be photocopied

End of Spelling Quiz

End of Book Test

(1) **Add <u>prefixes</u> to make a word that <u>matches each definition</u>.**

An explorer among the stars is an .... naut.

Your life story written by yourself is an .... biography.

A big lorry that moves things is a .... porter.

1 mark

(2) **Rewrite the sentences below changing every <u>underlined</u> word for an <u>antonym</u>, and every word in <u>bold</u> for a <u>synonym</u>.**

Mark was a <u>miserable</u> boy who <u>never</u> smiled. He **liked** football, which he **frequently** played with his friends. He couldn't **tolerate** being indoors in <u>foul</u> weather.

....

....

....

.... 1 mark

(3) **Identify the <u>verb form</u> of the <u>underlined verbs</u> in the sentence.**

┌─────────────────────────┐   ┌─────────────────────────┐
│ ....simple past.......... │   │ .... │
└─────────────────────────┘   └─────────────────────────┘

It <u>was</u> four o'clock. We <u>were packing</u> up when I suddenly <u>looked</u> round to find that Rex <u>had vanished</u>, seemingly into thin air.

┌─────────────────────────┐   ┌─────────────────────────┐
│ .... │   │ .... │
└─────────────────────────┘   └─────────────────────────┘

1 mark

4 Two of the following sentences <u>link the clauses correctly</u> and two don't. Tick the two which are <u>correct</u>.

The dog barked, so the cat ran up the tree. ☐

The dog barked the cat ran up the tree. ☐

The dog barked, the cat ran up the tree. ☐

The dog barked; the cat ran up the tree. ☐

☐ 1 mark

5 <u>Underline</u> the <u>subjects</u> and <u>circle</u> the <u>objects</u> in these two sentences.

I love diplodocus the most out of all

the dinosaurs. Their long, graceful

necks fascinate me.

☐ 1 mark

6 Explain why there is a <u>colon</u> in this sentence.

We bought these ingredients: snail slime, nettles and cuckoo spit.

....

☐ 1 mark

7 Add the appropriate '<u>able</u>' or '<u>ible</u>' suffix to complete each word below. Then write a <u>sentence</u> that uses each word.

unintellig.......................... inevit..........................

....

....

☐ 1 mark

End of Book Test

94

8 Rewrite the passage below, linking the ideas by <u>time and place</u>. <u>Underline</u> any <u>linking words</u>, <u>phrases</u> or <u>clauses</u> that you use.

Vic was out running. A lorry drove past. She heard a helicopter.

....

....

....

1 mark

9 The sentences below use ellipsis and repetition to make them effective. <u>Underline</u> an example of <u>repetition</u>, and write out an example of <u>ellipsis</u>.

We marched up the hills and we marched down the hills; we marched through streams and through swamps. Someone pleaded that we camp for the night; the Captain said we couldn't — at least, not yet. Someone said we couldn't go on; the Captain said we must.

An example of an ellipsis is ....

....

1 mark

10 Rewrite the passage below with the <u>correct punctuation</u> and <u>capital letters</u>.

"let's go" Said Eve, "picking up her bags, or we'll miss the train".

....

....

2 marks

© CGP — not to be photocop

11 Rewrite the sentence below by <u>removing the conjunction</u> and replacing it with an <u>appropriate punctuation mark</u>.

John is very musical but Kevin is tone-deaf.

.... 1 mark

12 Add a <u>relative clause</u> with the <u>correct punctuation</u> to each sentence.

The dog ....

.... was eventually found safe and well.

Jenny ....

....would eat apples and bananas. 2 marks

13 Rewrite these sentences with the correct punctuation.

Mums favourite vegetable's were tomatoe's and potatoes'.

....

....

Both spacecrafts wings were smashed by the meteors impact.

....

.... 1 mark

14 Circle the <u>correct spelling</u> in each underlined pair of words.

He was an <u>aggressive</u> / <u>agresive</u> and <u>desparate</u> / <u>desperate</u> man.

The <u>acommodation</u> / <u>accommodation</u> is <u>availible</u> / <u>available</u>. 1 mark

End of Book Test

15 Label each sentence '**P**' for <u>passive voice</u> and '**A**' for <u>active voice</u>. Rewrite the <u>active sentence as passive</u>, and the <u>passive as active</u>.

The terrified kid was pounced upon by the ravenous tiger. ☐

....

The golf ball broke the porch window. ☐

....

The dirty water was poured carefully into a filter. ☐

☐

.... 2 marks

16 Rewrite this sentence with correct <u>punctuation</u> and <u>capital letters</u>. The underlined phrase is a <u>quotation</u>.

It said <u>open this way up</u> moaned tony and the arrow on the box

pointed downwards so I stood on my head to open it and fell over

....

.... ☐

.... 1 mark

17 Write a sentence that is linked to the first sentence by <u>cause</u>, <u>addition</u>, <u>contrast</u> or <u>condition</u>. <u>Underline</u> the link and write the type of link you have used ('cause', 'addition', etc.) in the box.

Phoebe loves books about history. ....

....

Type of link: (....) ☐

1 mark

18 Rewrite the sentences below, correcting the <u>homophones</u> that are wrong.

I woodn't go any father if I whirr you. No-one's lived their accept

ghosts for sentries. When Dad past it the other knight, he herd

growns coming from the sellers, two. ....

....

....

.... 1 mark

19 The sentence below contains <u>two verbs</u> which could be
written in the <u>subjunctive but aren't</u>. Cross out these
verbs and replace them with the <u>subjunctive forms</u>.

If he was to visit the museum, I would suggest that he goes on a

quiet day as it can get extremely busy. 2 marks

20 Write three different sentences. In each one use a <u>modal verb</u>
to show either <u>possibility</u>, <u>ability</u> or <u>obligation</u>.

possibility ....

....

ability ....

....

obligation ....

.... 2 marks

I scored [ ] out of 25.   😟 ☑   🙂 ☑   😃 ☑

End of Book Test

Glossary

Active Sentence — A sentence in which the **subject** does something to the **object**, e.g. I opened the window. You ate the apple.

Adverb — A word that describes a **verb**, an **adjective** or other **adverbs**.

Adverbial — A group of words that behaves like an **adverb**.

Antonyms — Words that mean the opposite, e.g. **loud** and **quiet**.

Clause — Part of a sentence that contains a **subject** and a **verb**.

Conjunction — A word or phrase that **joins** two parts of a sentence.

Determiner — Tells you if a **noun** is **general** or **specific**, e.g. I would like <u>a</u> drink. I would like <u>that</u> drink.

Direct Speech — The **actual words** the speaker says.

Main clause — A clause that **makes sense** on its own, e.g. <u>We play outside</u> when it is not raining.

Object — The part of the sentence having **something done to it**.

Passive Sentence — A sentence in which something is done to the **subject**, e.g. The window was opened. The apple was eaten.

Phrase — A group of words usually without a **verb**.

Pronoun — A word used to **replace** a **noun**, e.g. **it, we, you**.

Reported Speech — A **description** of someone's speech.

Subject — The person or thing **doing the verb**.

Subordinate clause — A clause that **doesn't make sense** on its own, e.g. We play outside <u>when it is not raining</u>.

Synonyms — Words that mean the same, e.g. **large** and **big**.

Glossary

PUNCTUATION MARKS

Apostrophes — show **missing letters** and **possession**.   '

Brackets — **separate extra information** in a sentence.   ( )

Colons — **introduce** some **lists** and **join clauses**.   :

Commas — used in **lists**, to **join clauses**, to separate **extra information** and after **fronted adverbials**.   ,

Dashes — **separate extra information** in a sentence.   —

Exclamation marks — show **exclamations**, **commands** or **strong emotions**.   !

Hyphens — used to **join words** or **add** a **prefix**.   -

Inverted commas — show **direct speech**.   " "

Semi-colons — separate **long items** in **lists** and **join clauses**.   ;

VERB FORMS

Simple <u>Past</u> — I <u>**ate**</u>, you <u>**ate**</u>, etc.

Simple <u>Present</u> — I <u>**eat**</u>, you <u>**eat**</u>, etc.

<u>Past</u> Progressive — I <u>**was**</u> eating, you <u>**were**</u> eating, etc.

<u>Present</u> Progressive — I <u>**am**</u> eating, you <u>**are**</u> eating, etc.

<u>Past</u> Perfect — I <u>**had**</u> eaten, you <u>**had**</u> eaten, etc.

<u>Present</u> Perfect — I <u>**have**</u> eaten, you <u>**have**</u> eaten, etc.

Imperative — **Do** your homework!, **Tidy** the lounge, etc.

Subjunctive — If I **were**, I insisted he **go**, etc.

Answers

Grammar

Section 1 – Word Classes

Pages 4 and 5 – Nouns: Subjects and Objects

1. You should have circled: **elephants**; **Martin**; **Zane**; **Poppy, Joe and Ella**; **my sister**; **Ben and Amanda**

2. The following sentences should be ticked:
    My dad grows tomatoes.
    Nitin moves his shoulders.
    She closed the door when she left.

3. I — **me, you** — you, he — **him**, **she** — her, it — **it**, we — **us**, the**y** — **them**

4. Subject pronouns: **We, I**
    Object pronouns: **them, it**

5. Any suitable explanation. Example:
    The word 'Me' is an object pronoun and shouldn't be used for the subject of the sentence. The correct subject pronoun is 'I'.

Pages 6-8 – Word Class and Word Function

1. weekly is an **adjective**
    low is an **adverb**
    straight is an **adverb**
    daily is an **adverb**

2. Any suitable answers with explanations. Examples:
    noun — I think this because: **it comes after a determiner, and ends in 's' like a plural noun.**
    verb — I think this because: **'was wimbling' looks like a past progressive verb form.**

3. Any suitable sentence using the word 'wimble'.
    Examples:
    The beanstalk looked wimble in the sun. (adjective)
    He was walking wimbly down the road. (adverb)

4. determiner, conjunction, pronoun, determiner, determiner, pronoun

5. There are lots of possible answers to this question. Make sure yours contains sentences including the given words. Examples:
    I think that people **will like my cakes**. ('that' is a conjunction)
    These trousers **are more expensive than the other ones**. ('these' is a determiner)
    I quite like these socks, but I can't stand those. ('those' is a pronoun)

6. Any suitable sentence which uses the given words in a different word class. Examples:
    noun — Let's try him on his mobile.
    verb — We may need to book a table.

7. Any suitable explanation. Example:
    Normally, 'but' is a conjunction, but in this expression it is used as both a verb ('but') and a noun ('buts'). (It has a similar structure to a sentence like 'Give me no chips').

Pages 9-11 – Synonyms and Antonyms

1. good: sing, <u>great</u>, assist, <u>kind</u>, <u>excellent</u>, happy, saint
    pretty: <u>beautiful</u>, <u>attractive</u>, neat, sparkle, <u>lovely</u>, <u>cute</u>
    sharp: point, <u>piercing</u>, <u>acute</u> (e.g. an acute pain = a sharp pain), <u>razor-edged</u>, unpleasantness
    bright: white, <u>gleaming</u>, shine, <u>glaring</u>, <u>intelligent</u>, <u>cheerful</u>
    poor: <u>inadequate</u>, weakness, <u>feeble</u> (e.g. a feeble attempt = a poor attempt), <u>ineffective</u>, hungry, <u>penniless</u>

2. Any suitable synonyms for the words. Examples:
    small — **miniature, tiny**
    finish (verb) — **complete, end**
    dull — **drab, boring**
    trip (noun) — **outing, journey**
    stone — **rock, pebble**
    brave — **courageous, gallant**
    laugh (verb) — **chuckle, giggle**

3. Any suitable synonyms for the underlined words. Examples:
    moving — **charging, stampeding, running**
    big — **enormous, gigantic, huge, colossal**
    said — **whispered, mouthed, panted, pleaded**

4. Any suitable sentences using antonyms of the underlined words. Examples:
    Gwen **scowled** as the clowns began their **boring** routine.
    Each **morning** at **sunrise**, the Inca priest turned to the **east**.
    The road through the forest was **narrow** and **winding**.
    Niall was **keen** to go and **rushed** down the road.

5. There are lots of possible answers to this question. Examples:
    friend (noun)
    Synonyms: mate, ally, partner, pal, chum
    Antonyms: enemy, stranger, foe, adversary
    give (verb)
    Synonyms: donate, offer, hand, impart, bequeath
    Antonyms: take, steal, pinch, retain, keep, receive
    quickly (adverb)
    Synonyms: fast, rapidly, speedily, hastily, hurriedly
    Antonyms: slowly, gradually, sluggishly, steadily

6. Any suitable sentence containing a word and its antonym. Example:
    Yesterday it was sunny, but today it is dull.

Answers

ction 2 – Verb Forms

ges 12 and 13 – Modal Verbs

Modal verbs of certainty:
She might be going out to lunch.
They will be taking a holiday next week.
We may live to regret that.

Modal verbs of ability:
I would do it if someone showed me how.
We can sit here; there's plenty of room.
She could climb it if she wanted to.

Modal verbs of obligation:
He was suggesting I should tidy my desk.
We must get to the airport early today.

Any suitable sentences that use modal verbs to express certainty and obligation. Examples:
They will take the dog for a walk.
You should apologise for your behaviour.

You should have circled: **might**, **may**
You should have underlined: **should**, **must**, **should**

Any suitable modal verbs. Examples:
You could keep guinea pigs in a hutch, but it **would** be nicer if they **could** run about. They **can** get sick in a small cage. You **should** put them in a larger run as they **could** do with a lot of exercise to keep them fit. They **must** have water and plenty of hay. Keep two together, or they **might** be lonely or sad.

There are lots of possible answers to this question. Example:
I might decide to become a rockstar, but I should warn you that I can only sing one song.

ges 14 and 15 – The Subjunctive

Not certain to happen:
I insist that they be informed of this development.
I requested that she not be prosecuted for the offence.
Your recommendation, madam, that the rules be relaxed is frankly unthinkable.
They suggested that I go home directly.

Alternative reality:
Oh dear! If only I were a tidier person!
If he were a gentle cat, I'd stroke him.
If you were to move school, I'd miss you.
We'd go out if you were properly dressed.
"If he were more amenable," I said, "I'd help him."

If she <u>were</u> willing to speak, I would let her speak.
I suggested that he <u>consult</u> a lawyer.
If she <u>were</u> embarrassed, she would show it.

3. Any suitable subjunctive forms. Examples:
If I **were** you, I would not fight with James.
His insistence that the building **be** torn down was ignored.
It is out of the question that this newspaper **print** that story.
If Jenny **were** more resilient, she might have weathered this storm.
I'd rather have stayed at home, if truth **be/were** told.
The judge ordered that the defendant no longer **be** detained.

4. There are lots of possible answers to this question. Make sure yours contains a subjunctive.

Pages 16 and 17 – Verb Forms – Recap

1. You should have circled: **hurry up**, **move**, **stop**, **make sure**, **pass**

2. There are lots of possible answers to this question. Examples:
Stop talking while I'm talking.
Sit down on the carpet.
Put your coat on before you go outside.

3. Any suitable sentences using the given verb forms. Examples:
I skip across the playground.
I am skipping across the playground.
I skipped across the playground.
I was skipping across the playground.
I have skipped across the playground.
I had skipped across the playground.
I must skip across the playground.
I wouldn't skip across the playground if I were you.
Greg demanded that I skip across the playground.
Skip across the playground!

4. There are lots of possible answers to this question. Make sure yours includes at least one imperative and three other verb forms.

Pages 18 and 19 – Verb Forms in Action

1. past perfect verb: had gone, had fallen
present perfect verb: I've been
subjunctive verb form: were
present progressive form: I'm being
imperative form: Be (thankful)
past progressive form: was riding

2. There are lots of possible answers to this question. Make sure yours includes a variety of verb forms.

3. There are lots of possible answers to this question. Make sure yours refers to at least three of the verb forms you used in your answer to Question 2.

Answers

Section 3 – Phrases and Clauses

Pages 20 and 21 – Modifiers

1. You should have circled: **lawn, hot, John, she was determined to complete the task**

2. Any suitable modifiers. Examples:
   The **incredibly** strong wind.
   The house **next to the mysterious green lake**.
   Zac, **who was dressed as a ghost**, suddenly appeared.

3. Any suitable explanations and suggested improvements. Examples:
   The meaning is unclear because **it could mean exercising frequently will make you happier; or it could mean when you do exercise, it often makes you feel happier.**
   Ways to reword the sentence: '**Frequent exercise makes you feel happier**' OR '**You often feel happier when you exercise**'.

4. Any suitable explanation. Example:
   Person B has understood the phrase 'called Steve' to be a modifier of 'girl' rather than 'mouse'. As 'Steve' is an unusual name for a girl, it's odd to assume that she is called Steve rather than the mouse.

Pages 22 and 23 – Modifying the Subject

1. Any suitable answer. Examples:
   Mr Clay, a smart dresser in his youth, now wore only jeans.
   Wimbledon, a district of south-west London, is home to a world-famous tennis tournament.
   Roald Dahl, a much-loved children's author, was born in Wales to Norwegian parents.

2. Any suitable answers. Examples:
   A stern and unforgiving person, Mrs Moody was not a woman to be trifled with.
   Overrun with violence and crime, Grantwich was about to undergo a great change.
   Tired and thirsty, the elephants went back to the oasis.
   A source of misery for so many people, the war was a source of adventure for Arthur. *(Make sure your modifier describes the 'war', which is the subject of the sentence. If it describes Arthur (e.g. 'Having always longed for excitement...'), it's a misplaced modifier.)*

Pages 24 and 25 – Phrases and Clauses – Characters

1. Three adjectives: handsome, clever, rich
   Noun phrase: 'some of the best blessings of existence'
   Adverbial: 'with very little to distress or vex her.'

2. There are lots of possible answers to this question. Example:
   Libby Brown, witty, talented and kind, a friend to almost everyone she met, had lived nearly eleven years in the world knowing that she was widely respected and adored.

3. A fearful man, all in coarse grey, <u>with a great iron on his leg</u>. A man <u>with no hat</u>, and <u>with broken shoes</u>, and <u>with an old rag tied round his head</u>. A man <u>who had been soaked in water, and smothered in mud, and lamed by stones, and cut by flints, and stung by nettles, and torn by briars; who limped, and shivered, and glared, and growled; and whose teeth chattered in his head as he seized me by the chin</u>.
   Any suitable explanation. Example:
   The modifiers help the reader to picture what the man looks like and how he might behave. They also make the reader wary of the man and worried for the boy.

4. There are lots of possible answers to this question. Make sure yours includes plenty of modifiers to build-up the description. Example:
   She had a strange, threatening face. A face that showed malice in every feature. A face that spoke treachery and vice. A face that you knew could sink a thousand ships by a flicker of an eye or a twitch of the nose.

Pages 26 and 27 – Phrases and Clauses – Settings

1. You should have underlined: **in front of which a sandstone wall forms a barrier against high tides**, **beyond which visitors can see an attractive stretch of the North Wales coastline**.

2. There are lots of possible answers to this question. Make sure yours starts with a noun phrase that modifies the name of your town, and also includes at least two relative clauses beginning with a preposition.

3. You should have underlined: **rushed by**, **whistled**, **made strange noises**
   Any suitable answer. Example:
   They make the landscape seem spooky and mysterious.
   You should have underlined: **through which she was passing on a strip of dry land**.
   Any suitable answer. Example:
   It tells us that Mary feels frightened and is desperate for the journey to be over.

4. There are lots of possible answers to this question. Make sure yours rewrites the passage from Question 3 so that it has a more cheerful mood.

Answers

ction 4 – Linking Ideas

ges 28 and 29 – Ways to Link Ideas

Beside the stream was a small cottage. — place
Tidy it — whether you want to or not! — condition
We'll go out whenever you're ready. — time
She likes coffee; I, however, like tea. — contrast
They went for a walk despite the rain. — contrast
We ate pizza as well as salad for lunch. — addition
Provided that I can afford it, we'll go. — condition
Put it down gently because it's fragile. — cause
I disliked the visit, whereas she didn't. — contrast
I've had enough; moreover, I feel sick. — addition

Any suitable rewritten sentences using a linking word or phrase. Examples:
Some people agree with me, whereas others don't.
I want to go swimming as long as the weather is fine.
Some people approve of homework because they think it's useful.

There are lots of possible answers to this question. Make sure yours include the types of link given in brackets.

ges 30 and 31 – Linking Ideas in Different nres

Most of the links in this text are to do with time and place.
Time: 'The following morning', 'when...', 'First', 'by the time', 'Suddenly'
Place: 'From a little way off', 'all around her', 'In the distance', 'towards her', 'overhead'

Most of the links in this text are to do with contrast, addition and cause.
Contrast: 'Despite', 'Unlike'
Addition: 'Indeed', 'and', 'Furthermore'
Cause: 'thanks to', 'as a consequence'

In story writing, you tend to find more links of **time and place**, whereas in report writing you tend to find more links of **contrast, addition and cause**. I think this might be because in stories it is important to show **when and where things are happening**, whereas in reports it is important to show **why things happen, and how one thing compares with another**.

In a persuasive text you'd expect to find links of addition (e.g. 'Furthermore', 'also', Indeed', 'As well as...') , condition (e.g. 'If', 'unless', 'As long as...') and cause (e.g. 'since', 'became', 'due to', 'thanks to'). Other answers are possible but you should be able to explain your answer.

Pages 32 and 33 – Linking Ideas Across Paragraphs

1. Any suitable linking word or phrase with an accompanying explanation of what it is linking. Examples:
   however — contrast
   It links the information about female lions to the information about male lions in the previous paragraph.
   In addition — addition
   It links the paragraph to the previous paragraph about female lions.

2. There are lots of possible answers to this question. Make sure yours contains three paragraphs which are clearly linked by a word or phrase.

Pages 34 and 35 – Repetition and Ellipsis

1. I've seen the film but Rita hasn't. **E**
   He tried this, he tried that and he tried the other. Nothing worked. **R**
   They sold the house because they wanted to. **E**
   Anne has eaten too much, and Mia too little. **E**
   I want to go, I want to go now and I want to go for a long time. **R**
   Any suitable sentences showing repetition and ellipsis. Examples:
   I searched in the kitchen, under the stairs, and in the hallway. My wellies were nowhere to be found.
   He hated the rain; he hated the wind; he hated the cloud.

2. There are several possible answers to this question. Example:
   "Come on. Let's go to Dave's."
   "I don't want to. It was really boring last time."
   "I know it was, but it might not be this time. And if we don't go, we'll just be bored here."

3. The extract contains repetition of the phrase 'one last push'.
   There are lots of possible answers to this question. Example:
   The repetition is meant to inspire the team to keep trying as hard as they can, to keep the players focused and to hammer home the fact that it will soon all be over.

Pages 36 and 37 – Summary of Cohesive Devices

1. Any suitable rewriting of the text using cohesive devices to make the text flow better. Any suitable explanation of why a certain cohesive device has been used.

2. Any suitable rewriting of the text using different cohesive devices to make the text more sophisticated.

Answers

3. There are lots of possible answers to this question. Make sure yours includes a summary of what you have learned about cohesive devices as well as when and why they should be used.

Section 5 – Writing Style

Pages 38 and 39 – Active and Passive Voice

1. The cat chased the mouse. **A**
   The bird was caught by a net. **P**
   Sam was allowed to do the task. **P**
   Josh worked hard at school. **A**
   Megan enjoyed playing rugby. **A**
   Jan was told off by her mum. **P**
   He was eaten by a crocodile. **P**
   She slipped in the mud. **A**
   We were beaten by enemies. **P**
   They were cheated out of it. **P**

2. Any suitable rewriting of the sentences from active to passive. Examples:
   The trumpet was played by Nathan.
   All the grass was eaten by one goat and two sheep.
   The article in the paper was read by lots of people.

3. There are lots of possible answers to this question. Make sure yours includes the passive voice.

4. The carvings were made in prehistoric times. — We don't know who did the action
   Fruit should be eaten daily. — It applies to everyone
   A sign will be put up in the morning. — It's not important who did the action
   I'm afraid the window has been smashed. — Avoiding responsibility

Pages 40 and 41 – Choosing between Active and Passive

1. A piece of beetroot was cut into a 1 cm cube. Some water was poured into a beaker until it was 5 cm deep. A cube of beetroot was put into the beaker and a stopwatch was started. A sample of the water was taken from the beaker after two minutes had passed.

2. Any suitable summary of the what the witnesses saw, written in the passive voice.

3. Any suitable explanation of why passage 2 would be better if it was written in the active voice. Example: I think passage **2** should be written in active voice because **we want to know who is doing what. The active voice sounds more dramatic and exciting than the passive voice.**

Pages 42-44 – Formal and Informal Register

1. A letter of complaint about a game you bought that arrived broken. **F**
   Trying to persuade your head teacher to reduce class homework. **F**
   Writing in your own diary about a school trip that you really disliked. **I**
   Writing an article for a school newsletter about a school trip. **F**
   Sending an email to a friend about arranging a birthday party. **I**
   Writing a newspaper report about school traffic in your area. **F**
   Writing to parents asking them to park more carefully near school. **F**
   Any suitable examples of a situation in which you'd use formal language and a situation in which you'd use informal language. Examples:
   Interviewing your teacher for the school newspaper. **F**
   Sending your friend a message about going to the park. **I**

2. Any suitable answers that use informal language. Examples:
   The weather is hotter today, don't you think?
   He's gonna be late, isn't he?
   Calm down — I'll be with you in a minute.

3. There are lots of possible answers to this question. Make sure yours uses plenty of features of informal language.

4. Any suitable rewriting of the text using more formal language.

Page 45 – Grammatical Features of Different Genres

1. A: **poetry** — Words and phrases written in a non-standard order. Each line starts with a capital letter.
   B: **report** — Written in the third person with technical vocabulary. Present tense.
   C: **instructions** — Sentences start with an imperative verb. Written in the second person.
   D: **recount** — Adverbials show the sequence of events. Written in the first person and past tense.

End of Grammar Quiz

Pages 46 and 47

1. A small man who came in and picked up the book Mia and Patrick tidied the extremely messy room before lunch.
   [1 mark]

Skating is **hard**, and the first time I went, I fell (hard) on the ice.
Clara drove extremely (fast) because it was a very **fast** car.
[1 mark]

There are lots of possible answers to this question. Example:
As I am **nice**, I won't tell Mum you broke her **oldest** vase. *[1 mark]*

There are lots of possible answers to this question. Example:
I **would** not pick that plant; it **might** be poisonous. You **could** get very sick, and you **may** end up in hospital.
[1 mark]

If I **were** a better runner, I might try a marathon. They insisted **that** the ice cream **be** served immediately. *[1 mark]*

Any suitable answer that includes a past progressive form (e.g. 'was eating' or 'were running'), a simple past form (e.g. 'ate' or 'ran') and a present perfect form (e.g. 'has swooped' or 'have decided').
Example:
While the dinosaur was running along, a scarlet-feathered bird swooped down and asked, "Have you eaten the professor?"
[1 mark]

Example:
Theo, who keeps chickens, enjoys cooking with the eggs they lay. *[1 mark]*

Many trees were knocked down by the landslide.
[1 mark]

Example:
Please may I have a new exercise book, as mine is full. *[1 mark]*

). Any noun phrase including a relative clause; for example, 'a vast desert over which the sun shone endlessly'.
[1 mark]

nctuation

ction 6 – Sentence Punctuation

ge 48 – Colons for Lists

We had everything we needed for the cake: eggs, flour, butter and sugar.
The results of our birdwatch were five starlings, two sparrows, three robins and one crow.
His acting roles came in this order: 'Deadly Hamsters', 'Night of the Killer Crabs', 'Deadly Hamsters 2' and 'Revenge of Fluffy'.

2. The following people are coming to my party: Tom, Yasmin, Ellen, Tomas and Deena.
They speak Spanish in the following countries: Chile, Argentina, Mexico, Peru and Bolivia.

Page 49 – Using a Semi-Colon in Lists

1. Any suitable answers. Examples:
The guest list was unusual: an Albanian juggler called Pavel; **a Spanish artist called Teresa; an Irish dancer called Seamus; and a French politician called Pierre.**
The police inspector had four suspects: a singer, who was spotted near the robbery; **a gang of teenagers, who had vandalised a nearby billboard; an elderly lady, who had some suspicious items in her handbag; and the shop's owner, who had recently been having money troubles.**
My dream house would contain the following things: a robot that brought cheeseburgers to my bedroom; **a swimming pool filled with melted chocolate; a room full of arcade machines; and a TV as big as the living room wall.**

Pages 50 and 51 – Semi-Colons to Join Clauses

1. That ride was too scary; I'll be sticking to the dodgems in future.
I like my friends to be funny and clever; I'll make an exception for you.

2. Any suitable answers that contain two main clauses linked by a semi-colon. Examples:
The cat looked quite ill; I took it to the vet.
Carla was angry with me; I didn't know what I'd done.

3. You should have put a tick next to these sentences:
Wait for the last day of the sales; they end on Friday.
I told Jabir the match was cancelled; he turned up anyway.
The traffic was terrible; we arrived with a minute to spare.
You should have put a cross next to these sentences:
Evie, Ben and Arthur; you're all in my team.
You'll get plenty to eat; at the barbecue.

4. Any suitable answers. Examples:
The town had withstood the siege for eight weeks; meanwhile **the stone city had crumbled.**
We saw a trail of crumbs; obviously **we followed them to see where they'd lead.**
I've been spending more money than I earn; therefore I might run out of money soon.
The weight lifter has shown incredible strength and determination; however, her sportsmanship has been sadly lacking.

Answers

Pages 52 and 53 – Colons to Introduce a Clarification

1. Three children were picked for the running team: Anwen, Rob and Jamie. (**explains which children were picked for the running team**)
The dog was in disgrace: there were ripped clothes everywhere. (**explains what the dog had done**)
Caitlin was first in the race: she led from the start. (**explains how Caitlin had won the race**)

2. Any suitable answers. Examples:
I had laid out my clothes for the next day: **a navy blue suit.**
My brother is afraid of so many things: **spiders, birds and clowns.**
I knew why the sweet jar was empty: **I'd eaten them all the day before.**
I shall be giving you a special gift: **a handmade bracelet.**

3. You should have put a tick next to these sentences:
The answer is simple: we eat our way out!
There are three people in my class who come to school by bus: Josie, Bhalraj and Imran.
She knew one thing: she would never go back.
You should have put a cross next to these sentences:
Mr Williams is our neighbour: his daughter is called Jessica.
Deep in the forest: under the old oak tree, the treasure was buried.

4. I live close to a lake: I've never swum in it. — different punctuation needed
I need you to help me with changing the tyre: on my bike. — no colon needed
Snakes are reptiles cold-blooded: and egg-laying. — colon in wrong place

5. There are lots of possible answers to this question. Make sure you've written one sentence that uses a colon to introduce an explanation, and one that uses a colon to introduce a specific example. Examples:
Walter chose to get a goldfish: he wanted a low-maintenance pet.
There's only one flavour of ice cream I like: vanilla.

Section 7 – Commas and Apostrophes

Pages 54 and 55 – Apostrophes for Contraction and Possession

1. When it's Emily's turn to do the washing up, she's nowhere to be found. — 2 apostrophes for contraction, 1 apostrophe for possession
Jordan's dog lost its ball and won't stop howling. — 1 apostrophe for contraction, 1 apostrophe for possession
We weren't allowed sweets at Holly's, but Kim's mum doesn't mind. — 2 apostrophes for contraction, 2 apostrophes for possession
I don't know who's sitting in Ellie's seat, but they'll be in trouble when she gets back. — 3 apostrophes for contraction, 1 apostrophe for possession

2. Are not
who will, I am
they are, he has

3. the octopus's tentacles
the children's playground
the foxes' den
my sisters' room

4. Thomas' sister does'nt know whose coming.
correct sentence: Thomas's sister doesn't know who's coming.
My cat keep's leaving it's fur on Mums cushions.
correct sentence: My cat keeps leaving its fur on Mum's cushions.
The teacher's car park at my school is'nt very large.
correct sentence: The teachers' car park at my school isn't very large.
There going to leave Agnes' song out of the show.
correct sentence: They're going to leave Agnes's song out of the show.

Pages 56 and 57 – Commas to Punctuate Adverbials

1. You should have added commas to these sentences:
After carefully preparing a canvas, the artist began to paint.
The train pulled out leaving the passenger behind.
The robin was hopping, completely unafraid, nearer and nearer to the man.
On the other side of the valley, the vegetation was much greener.
Bob finally got there and, to his astonishment, he was the first one to arrive.
After watching the film, the girls discussed it over a cup of tea and a biscuit.

Answers

2. Any suitable answers. Examples:
   The boy, having waited for what seemed like ages, edged out from behind the skip.
   The fawn entered the glade slowly and cautiously.
   A small, shivering figure walked down the path without a backward glance at the house.
   The knight set off, riding swiftly into the night, on the adventure of a lifetime.

3. There are lots of possible answers to this question. Examples:
   The kitten, exhausted from playing with the ball of wool, fell asleep on Miles's lap.
   The girls ran away after breaking the window.

Pages 58 and 59 – Commas to Avoid Ambiguity

1. The treasure chest contained gold, coins, diamonds and pearls.
   The class were visited by Mrs King, a retired doctor, and a juggler.
   I'm ready to paint, Mark.
   At the village green, people are holding a barbecue.
   Molly, the school caretaker, is locking the gates.

2. Any suitable explanations. Examples:
   The comma makes it clearer that Ameena and I, not the fox, had the telescope.
   The comma makes it clearer that he ate the cake, but not his homework.
   The commas make it clearer that I was with Rocky, Lola and some dogs rather than just two dogs called Rocky and Lola.

3. Any drawings that show that the sausages, as well as the vegetables, are green in the first picture.

Page 60 – Parenthesis

1. Any suitable answers. Examples:
   Clara's aunt (who few people liked) scowled at the children.
   Clara's aunt — such a kind woman — gave sweets to the children.
   Clara's aunt, her mother's sister, smiled at the children.

2. There are lots of possible answers to this question. Make sure yours include the three ways of punctuating a parenthesis. Examples:
   The book, a collection of fairy tales, was old and dusty.
   The book (which had lost several pages) was a collection of fairy tales.
   The book — a battered bundle of torn pages — was a collection of fairy tales.

Section 8 – Punctuation for Speech

Page 61 – Punctuating Dialogue

1. There are lots of possible answers to this question. Make sure yours includes correctly punctuated dialogue between two characters. Example:
   "What's happened, Eddie?" asked Sandra.
   "I tried dunking the ball, but I managed to dunk myself!"
   "You should be more careful, Eddie. You could have hurt yourself."
   "I know, but I was so close this time, Sandra."
   "Wait here and I'll go and get a ladder."
   "Please hurry up — I'm starting to feel dizzy."

Pages 62 and 63 – Reported Speech and Direct Speech

1. Any suitable rewriting of the sentences. Examples:
   Lily asked Ali if they had any rope because she thought they might need some.
   "I looked for some rope," Ali replied, "but I couldn't find any. We might have to improvise and take that sheet off the bed."

2. Any suitable rewriting of the passage. Example:
   Salma and Bo sat with the wizard while he told them how to get to the island.
   "Be careful in the boat," the wizard explained. "If you dip your hands or feet into the sea, the Mer-folk will know you're there and they'll try to destroy you."
   "Is there a way we can defend ourselves from the Mer-folk?" enquired Salma.
   "Would weapons be useful?" added Bo.
   The wizard explained that taking weapons would be a bad idea, as the Mer-folk would think they were hostile.
   "Should we take any food or gifts with us that we could give to the Mer-folk?" suggested Salma.
   "Yeah, that sounds like a good idea," agreed Bo.

Answers

Page 64 – Inverted Commas

1. Any suitable addition of inverted commas and explanation of why they have been used. Examples:
    Their last single 'Gobstopper Girls' wasn't very successful.
    The inverted commas are used to introduce the name of a song.
    Joanne's 'great deal' left me with no money and a pack of stale biscuits.
    The inverted commas are used to show that the speaker doesn't believe it was a great deal.
    Everyone knew about Elsa's 'secret' hiding place.
    The inverted commas are used to show that Elsa's hiding place isn't a secret.
    I played 'Ratty' in our school play, 'Wind in the Willows'.
    The inverted commas are used to introduce the name of a character in a play as well as the play's title.
    Animals which are active during the daytime are called 'diurnal'.
    The inverted commas are used to introduce a technical term.

Page 65 – Inverted Commas inside Inverted Commas

1. You should have underlined the following words:
    "My ship's called 'Sea Rover' — she's so fast," said the pirate, proudly.
    "It says here 'don't feed after midnight', but I did," moaned Jessica.
    "I think 'The Greatest Granny' is a brilliant book, don't you?" said Ava.
    You should have circled these words: **Sea Rover**, **don't feed after midnight**, **The Greatest Granny**

2. "I don't know why there was an explosion," panted Jim from where he was lying. "It says here 'heat the pot gently', and I'm sure that I did."

Section 9 – Paragraphs and Layout

Pages 66-68 – Improving Paragraphs

1. Any suitable rewriting of the paragraph to make it more organised. Example:
    Comets travel huge distances within the Solar System. Most comets visiting the Solar System travel from beyond the orbit of Neptune. Sungrazer comets travel so close to the Sun that they can be destroyed. The famous Halley's Comet doesn't get closer than 55,000,000 miles.

2. Any suitable paragraph written using the notes in the box. Example:
    Comets have a nucleus (centre) of frozen rock and ice. As a comet travels towards the Sun, the nucleus heats up and evaporates developing a 'coma' of hot, glowing gases. Near the Sun, the comet develops a long tail of gas and dust, which can be 90 million miles long, always pointing away from the Sun. It is these tails which gave us the word 'comet', or 'hairy star'.

3. It's important to present information to your reader in paragraphs which are well organised otherwise they may struggle to understand what you mean. It's good to start with a topic sentence to introduce what the paragraph is about. The information should be in a logical order, and if possible you should end your paragraph with some sort of conclusion.

4. There are lots of possible answers to this question, but the subheadings should be in a logical order.

5. Any suitable explanation of why you chose the order of subheadings in Question 4.
    For example, you may have chosen to start with 'Space' to introduce the whole topic. You may then have chosen to order the subheadings from large to small ('The Universe', 'Galaxies', 'The Solar System'...).
    Alternatively, you may have started with 'The Earth' because that is what the reader is most familiar with, followed by 'The Moon', and the 'The Solar System' etc.
    The important thing is to choose a sensible order which you can justify.

Page 69 – Bullet Points

1. Any suitable rewriting of the passage using bullet points. Example:
    Please observe tennis etiquette by:
    • replaying a point if you disagree about whether the ball was in or out.
    • congratulating your opponent if they play a good shot.
    • shaking hands with and thanking your opponent after a match.
    • remembering that it's only a game.

Pages 70 and 71 – Layout Devices

1. Any suitable answers. Examples:
    The subheadings in the text tell the reader what each section is about.
    The box helps to alert the reader to important information (the telephone number).
    The numbered list makes it clear what to do if you find an injured hedgehog.

Answers

2. There are lots of possible answers to this question. Make sure yours includes all the layout devices listed in the question.

End of Punctuation Quiz

Pages 72 and 73

1. He gave me the following gifts: a small white dog with black spots intended to be my travel companion; a large loaf of bread which I'd probably never finish; and a flask of raspberry lemonade. *[1 mark]*
(You may also have added extra punctuation to the answer shown above (e.g. punctuation to show parenthesis) but the colon and two semi-colons must be present to gain the mark.)

2. Elvis's brother's friend said, "Let's take old Sam's dog for a walk." OR (possibly, but less likely): Elvis's brothers' friend... *[1 mark]*

3. After a very long journey, Evie eventually got off the train at Brigg.
The thrush, singing like an angel, was perched on the tallest tree.
[1 mark]

. The left-hand sentence is telling Will not to pay. The right-hand sentence is telling someone not to pay Will.
[1 mark]

. commas, brackets and dashes *[1 mark]*

. There are lots of possible answers to this question. Example:
"Mum, I won the maths competition," said Salma proudly. *[1 mark]*

. There are lots of possible answers to this question. Example:
Dan asked his mum, groaning unconvincingly, whether he could miss school as his tummy hurt. *[1 mark]*

"That's my dog's ball," said Lucy, running up to the tall boy, "and your dog just chewed it up." *[1 mark]*

There was only one possible explanation: she'd been kidnapped.
Example explanation: **Colons are used to introduce an explanation.**
Today was a good day; tomorrow will be even better.
Example explanation: **Semi-colons are used when there's a close link between two main clauses.**
[2 marks for two correct punctuation marks with an appropriate explanation, or just 1 mark for 1 correct answer and explanation]

Spelling

Section 10 – Prefixes

Pages 74 and 75 – Roots and Prefixes from Greek and Latin

1. psych = the mind. E.g. psychology, psychotherapy, psyche, psychopath
ped = foot. E.g. pedestal, impediment, quadruped, pedal, centipede
photo = light. E.g. photocopy, photosynthesis, photographer
dorm = sleep. E.g. dormant, dormer
milli = 1000. E.g. millipede, milligram, millenium

2. 'mater' means **mother**
'bene' means **good or well**
'aqua' means **water**
'mort' means **dead**
'semi' means **half**
'phone' means **sound**

3. aero = air. E.g. aeroplane, aerodynamics, aerate, aerobics
anti = against. E.g. antisocial, antiseptic, antipathy
astro = star. E.g. astronomy, astrology, astronaut
bio = life. E.g. biology, biography, biodegradable
chrono = time. E.g. chronology, chronological, synchronise
cred = believe. E.g. incredible, credit, credulous
geo = Earth. E.g. geography, geometry, geology
graph = writing. E.g. photograph, calligraphy, autograph
omni = all. E.g. omnivore, omnipotent, omnibus
tele = far away. E.g. television, telephone, telecommunications
trans = across. E.g. transport, transform, transmit

Page 76 – Prefixes: 'em' and 'en'

1. to anger = **en**rage
to delight in = **en**joy
to make more bold = **em**bolden
to strengthen = **en**force

2. There are lots of possible answers to this question. Examples:
I was empowered to challenge his decision.
We were enclosed in a very small space.
We should try to protect endangered species.
He embodies the best things about our town.
I became entangled in a barbed wire fence.

3. entrust
encode OR encrypt
emphasise
enrol OR enlist

Answers

Page 77 – Prefixes: 'pre' and 'post'

1. **pre**arranged, **pre**historic, **post**humous, **post**pone, **pre**destined, **post**-mortem
   In **prehistoric** times, wolves and bears lived in Britain.
   The soldier who died in battle was awarded a **posthumous** medal for his bravery.
   The meal had been **prearranged** to coincide with the cousins' visit.
   Due to an outbreak of flu, we had to **postpone** the meeting.
   Harold thought he was **predestined** to be king because of a crown-shaped birthmark on his shoulder.
   The **post-mortem** revealed traces of arsenic in the body.

2. 'ante' means **before**
   'meridiem' means **midday**

Pages 78 and 79 – Prefixes That Require a Hyphen

1. The **ex-wrestler** was **self-employed**.
   The petrol station was **self-service**.
   Her **ex-husband** went on an **all-inclusive** holiday.

2. There are lots of possible answers to this question. Examples:
   She was too self-conscious to sing in front of the rest of the class.
   Her passion for football had become all-consuming.

3. **pre-Roman**, **re-enter**, **return**, **re-emphasise**, **disgrace**, **re-covered**, **mid-July**, **re-emerged**, **disappeared**

4. There needs to be a hyphen in 're-sign', as this verb is probably intended to mean 'sign again' rather than 'quit their jobs'.

Section 11 – Word Endings and Suffixes

Pages 80-82 – Suffixes: 'able' or 'ible'

1. preferable, understandable, justifiable, audible, credible, fixable

2. 'Suit' is a complete word.
   'Horr' is not a complete word.
   There is a related '-ation' word ('irritation').
   'Intellig' is not a complete word.
   'Agree' is a complete word.

3. feasible, feasibly, feasibility
   variable, variably, variability
   irritable, irritably, irritability
   visible, visibly, visibility
   excitable, excitably, excitability

4. There are lots of possible answers to this question. Examples:
   Unfortunately the toilets were not easily accessible.
   He bought a new reversible coat.
   Her failure to help him was contemptible behaviour.

5. serviceable, desirable, excusable, changeable

6. ill**egible**
   inv**incible**
   el**igible**
   inta**ngible**

7. Something that can't be believed is **unbelievable**.
   Example sentence: The amount of rubbish we've produced this weekend is **unbelievable**.
   Something that can't be conceived is **inconceivable**.
   Example sentence: I'm afraid it's **inconceivable** that England will win tonight.

Page 83 – Suffixes: Doubling the Consonant

1. **t**ransferred
   deferring
   preferable
   inferred
   conference
   referee

2. There are lots of possible answers to this question. Examples:
   If there's a **cancellation**, we may still get tickets.
   Working as a **counsellor**, he had helped many people.
   We **marvelled** at the beautiful sunset.
   They spent the evening **quarrelling** about household chores.

Section 12 – Confusing Words

Pages 84 and 85 – Homophones and Easily Confused Words

1. bridle
   serial
   prey
   patience

2. There are lots of possible answers to this question. Examples:
   She was not allowed out to play.
   I quite enjoy reading aloud.
   Bad acting can lessen the impact of a film.
   We had an interesting lesson about the Vikings.

3. **meet** (upper) and **meat** (lower)
   stationery (upper) and **stationary** (lower)

Answers

4. Examples:
   draft: the first version
   draught: **a movement of cool air in a room**
   morning: the first part of the day
   mourning: **a period of sadness after someone dies**
   alter: **to change**
   altar: table used in a church
   tire: run out of energy
   tyre: a rubber wheel outer
   waist: the part of the body between the ribs and the hips
   waste: unwanted material
   steal: take unlawfully
   steel: **hard material made from iron**

5. breathe
   weary / desert
   accept
   loose
   affect

age 86 – 'ice' or 'ise'?

. license
  advise
  practice
  devise

. There are lots of possible answers to this question.
  Examples:
  He had lost his driving licence.
  Jeremy didn't listen to his brother's advice.
  I love the guitar but I don't practise very often.
  She bought a new device for playing music.

ges 87-89 – Words From the Year 5/6 Spelling
st

What you've written for this depends on which words you know.

There are lots of possible answers to this question.
Examples:
cate**gory**: They had to make a special category for the film.
ceme**tery**: Her ancestors were all buried in the same cemetery.
secret**ary**: He was secretary of his football club.
necess**ary**: It's necessary to wear a seatbelt when the car is in motion.

ex**aggerat**e
a**wkwar**d
twelfth
nuisance

individual, language, restaurant, persuade, guarantee

sufficient, conscience, foreign, neighbour, mischievous, convenience

6. amateur, curiosity, nuisance, criticise, temperature, privilege, rhythm, disastrous

7. vegetable, familiar, average
   competition, definite, parliament
   sincerely, queue, dictionary

End of Spelling Quiz

Pages 90 and 91

1. Auto = **self**, omni = **all**, trans = **through**,
   tele = **far away**
   [1 mark]

2. post-1066 — after the Normans invaded England
   pre-lunch — e.g. **before we had eaten**
   post-war — after the fighting was over
   [1 mark]

3. ex-soldier, self-motivated, all-knowing *[1 mark]*

4. You should have ticked: preferably, irritably, intelligible
   You should have written: **audible, accessible, capable, sensibly, edible**
   [1 mark]

5. pleasure — **pleasurable**
   Example sentence: **I don't find my visits to the dentist very pleasurable.**
   knowledge — **knowledgeable**
   Example sentence: **I am very knowledgeable about cars.**
   [2 marks — 1 mark for each correctly spelled '-ble' word and example sentence where the word is used correctly]

6. You should have circled '**deferred**' and '**excellent**'.
   [1 mark]

7. Any sentence using the word (or a variant with a prefix/suffix) appropriately is correct. The word must be correctly spelled. Examples:
   I wasn't **affected** by the train delays.
   She didn't understand the **effect** of her actions.
   These conditions are **unacceptable**!
   I like every fruit **except** pineapple.
   [2 marks for 4 suitable sentences, or 1 mark if you have at least 2 suitable sentences]

8. My adv**ic**e is that you pract**is**e using this dev**ic**e every day. *[1 mark]*

End of Book Test

Pages 92-97

1. **astro**naut, **auto**biography, **trans**porter
   [1 mark]

Answers

2. There are lots of possible answers to this question. Example:
Mark was a **happy** boy who **always** smiled. He **enjoyed** football, which he **often** played with his friends. He couldn't **stand** being indoors in **fine** weather. *[1 mark]*

3. <u>were packing</u> – past progressive
<u>looked</u> – simple past
<u>had vanished</u> – past perfect
[1 mark]

4. You should have ticked the first and fourth sentences:
The dog barked, so the cat ran up the tree.
The dog barked; the cat ran up the tree.
[1 mark]

5. You should have underlined 'I' and '**Their long, graceful necks**'.
You should have circled '**diplodocus**' and '**me**'.
[1 mark]

6. A colon is used to introduce items in a list. *[1 mark]*

7. unintellig**ible** and inevit**able**.
Any suitable sentences to follow. Examples:
His speech was so slurred it was **unintelligible**.
He'd put so much in the bag, it was **inevitable** that it should break.
[1 mark]

8. Any passage with clear links of time and place. Example:
Vic was out running when, <u>all of a sudden</u>, a lorry drove past her <u>so close it nearly hit her</u>. <u>A few seconds later</u>, she heard a helicopter <u>overhead</u>.
[1 mark]

9. You could have underlined 'We marched' OR 'through'.
Examples of ellipses are: 'the Captain said we couldn't [camp for the night]' OR 'the Captain said we must [go on]'.
[1 mark]

10. "**Let's** go**,**" **s**aid Eve, picking up her bags, **"**or we'll miss the train."
[2 marks, or 1 mark if you've made one error of punctuation]

11. John is very musical**;** Kevin is tone-deaf. *[1 mark]*

12. There are lots of possible answers to this question. Examples:
The dog **that had run away** was eventually found safe and well.
Jenny**, who disliked oranges and grapes,** would eat apples and bananas.
[2 marks, or 1 mark for 1 relative clause correctly punctuated]

13. **Mum's** favourite **vegetables** were **potatoes** and **tomatoes**.
Both **spacecrafts'** wings were smashed by the **meteor's** impact.
[1 mark]

14. He was an (aggressive)/ agresive and desparate / (desperate) man.
The acommodation /(accommodation) is availible (available).
[1 mark]

15. The terrified kid was pounced upon by the raveno tiger. – **P**
As the active: **The ravenous tiger pounced upon terrified kid.**
The golf ball broke the porch window. – **A**
As the passive: **The porch window was broken by the golf ball.**
The dirty water was poured carefully into a filter.
As the active: **I** (or 'we', 'someone', any other subject) **poured the dirty water carefully into a filter.**
[2 marks for all sentences correctly labelled and rewritten, or 1 mark for 2 sentences correctly labelled and rewritten]

16. There are several possible answers to this question Example:
"It said '**open this way up'**, " moaned **T**ony, "and arrow on the box pointed downwards**,** so I stood my head to open it and fell over**!**" *[1 mark]*

17. There are lots of possible answers to this question Example:
She is not very interested in geography <u>though</u>.
Type of link: **contrast**
[1 mark]

18. I **wouldn't** go any **farther** if I **were** you. No-one's lived **there except** ghosts for **centuries**. When D **passed** it the other **night**, he **heard groans** coming from the **cellars, too**. *[1 mark]*

19. You should have changed '**was**' to '**were**' and 'go to '**go**'.
[2 marks for both verbs crossed out and change correctly, otherwise 1 mark for 1 verb crossed o and changed correctly]

20. Any appropriate sentences. Examples:
possibility: It **may** rain tomorrow.
ability: **Can** you swim a whole mile?
obligation: You really **should** help your dad when asks you to.
[2 marks for 3 correct sentences, otherwise 1 m for 2 correct sentences]